To Katie:
Best wishes,

The Last of the Whistler

by John Dashney

John Dashney

2003

WW

Wicklewood Books

Wicklewood Books
1932 Chemeketa, NE
Salem, Oregon 97301

(Wicklewood Books is an imprint of The Stage Within Your Mind)

First Edition, First Printing

ISBN: 0-9633236-3-6

Library of Congress Control Number:2002108363

Layout and design by DIMI PRESS

Cover art by Sheila Somerville

This one is for Mom and Dad,
Who always listened,
And for P.R. and the *Oregon Journal* crew:
We put ‘em out.

*"Inasmuch as ye have done it unto one
of the least of these my brethren,
ye have done it unto me."*

—Matthew 25:40

Chapter One: Armistice Eve

One day back in 1952, when I am ten years old, I ask my dad what he thinks is the best way to judge a man's character. I can no longer recall just why I ask him this, but I can still remember his answer.

He jangles a ring of keys in his right front pocket for a few seconds, and then he says, very slowly, "I suppose there are a great many ways, but I would say the best way to judge a man's character is by how well he treats those who don't have the power to hit him back."

My name is Alec Lewis. Come with me on a journey into the past.

It is Monday, November 10, 1952—the day before Armistice Day. The United States is at war in Korea, but we don't call it a war. It's a "police action"—whatever that is supposed to mean. Harry Truman is still President, but General Eisenhower has just been elected to replace him.

We are in Mrs. Foster's fifth-grade classroom at Cozine Elementary School in Morrisonville, Oregon. It is nine a.m. and we have just finished the Pledge of Allegiance, but twenty-nine of us—sixteen boys and thirteen girls—still stand at attention by our desks. Eight boys, including me, wear third-year cub scout uniforms, even though this is not our meeting day. Seven girls have on their new green girl scout outfits. All of us have red paper poppies pinned to our shirts or blouses. We take patriotism very seriously in 1952.

The thirtieth student, Mary Alice Patterson, walks slowly to the front of the room and turns to face us. She wears a red and white skirt and a blue blouse with the buddy poppy pinned to the breast pocket. She is going to recite John McCrae's poem, *In Flanders Fields,* in honor of her uncle, Quentin Patterson, who was killed in the First World War. Each year she does this, and it is sheer agony for her. But she does it because she is the only one in the class who lost a relative in that war, and her father insists all his children do it to honor their uncle's memory.

Her two older brothers handle the poem easily, so I am told, but Mary Alice is the smallest girl in the class and very quiet and shy. Her face is unremarkable, except for huge sad brown eyes that make her look like something we will see later on in Keane paintings. I have watched her try to recite that poem for three of the last four years.

I remember first grade because she only manages to stumble through, "In Flanders Fields the poppies grow, Between the cro—" And then she wets her pants. In the second grade she tries again, gets a little farther, and doesn't wet herself—as far as I can tell. In third grade we're in different rooms, so I don't know how she does. In 1951 she almost makes it. This year, on a whim, I decide to help her, and it changes my whole life.

I'm good at memorizing things, and that poem only has fifteen lines and about a hundred words. So I catch up to Mary Alice as she puts her bike in the stand before school and tell her that I know the poem by heart and will cue her if she gets in trouble. She gives me a look of surprise and then a slow, shy smile.

Now her big sad eyes are staring right at me as I silently recite along with her.

In Flanders Fields the poppies blow
Amid the crosses, row on row…

I try to smile encouragement while keeping my mouth synchronized with hers. I don't know how much I'm helping, but her voice grows stronger as she continues.

We are the dead, short days ago
We lived, felt dawn, saw sunset glow....

I try to imagine what her uncle might have been like. He must have been a lot older than her father, since most of our fathers serve in World War II. The First World War, to us, is Grandfather's War.

Loved and were loved, and now we lie
In Flanders Fields.

I remember her saying once that he was a fighter pilot, shot down in a dogfight over no man's land, and that it took two days for his body to be recovered. I wonder if he was killed on impact and what it would be like to fall out of the sky like a meteor. She must be thinking along the same lines, because I see tears as she finishes.

If you break faith with us who die.
We shall not sleep, though poppies grow
In Flanders Fields.

She blinks back the tears, smiles at me again, and her ordeal is over for another year.

Then I turn and see Mrs. Foster watching me. For an instant I fear I'm in trouble, but she gives me a quick hint of a smile and a barely perceptible nod, and I know she won't say anything. Still, I'm worried. Being anything more than civil to girls is still a year away for most of us, and I'll be teased big-time if anyone else notices. So I stay as far away from Mary Alice as I can for the rest of the day.

But when school is over, she follows me outside and waits for me to pull my bike from the stand. (Hey, we never bother to lock them in 1952.) "I called Mom this noon and told her I made it all the way through," she says. "I told her how you helped. She'd like you to come over. Can you?"

Go over to visit a girl? At her house? I start to shake my head.

Then she says, "She's made a big batch of cookies," and I begin to waver. "She says she'd like to thank you," Mary Alice adds, and then she tosses in the clincher. "They're chocolate chip! Big ones! With walnuts!"

Oooh man! For a big chocolate chip cookie with walnuts, I would kiss Mary Alice in front of the whole class! Heck! For a batch of 'em, I 'd do it in front of the whole school! Still, I try to look cool and think about it.

"I guess it would be okay," I admit. "But I'd have to call home from your place and check in."

"That's no problem. Do you know where I live?"

"Not exactly. Is it up on The Hill somewhere?"

"Only ten blocks. You can follow me."

So we pedal away from the school and I'm hoping no one else notices when I turn right instead of left on Yamhill Street and begin to climb The Hill. I suppose The Hill has a name, but to us it's just The Hill, and the people who live on it, of course, we call Hillbillies—though in truth they're some of the richest folks in town.

My bike is an old Columbia with fat balloon tires, while hers is one of the light new English-style three-speeds, with a low center bar to accommodate her skirt. She can gear down, so I have to stand and lean into it to stay with her. Of course she lives clear at the top, so all the way up I am thinking—those cookies had better be everything she says they are and more!

Her house is a new brick-and-wood ranch model, with a lawn that looks like a barber cares for it. But what grabs my attention is a big television antenna on the roof, with the tines pointing north to Portland. Oooh boy! Mary Alice can watch KPTV, the only television station in the state. Lucky dog! Only a handful of places can pick up their signal this far south.

Mrs. Patterson meets us at the back door, gives me a look that says, "Hmm, so *this* is Alec," and ushers us into the kitchen. I explain about phoning home, and she points to a phone on the counter. I pick it up and wait for the operator's voice.

"Number please."

"Eight-oh-one," I tell her.

"Thank you," and after two rings Mom is on the line.

"Oh?" she says when I explain where I am. "Visiting young ladies already? Is this serious?"

"Mom!" I can tell I'm turning red because I always blush easily. "Her mother invited me over for cookies. I, uh, helped her with a poem she had to recite this morning."

"Really? Well, that was very nice of you. You can stay a little while, but mind your manners, and I want you home before dark. You don't have a light on that bike of yours yet. And no more than two cookies! I'm fixing pork chops tonight, and I don't want you spoiling your appetite."

"Yes'm. Goodbye." Then I tell Mrs. Patterson that it's okay and I can stay for about half an hour, if it's all right with her.

"Half an hour will be fine," Mrs. Patterson says and sets out cookies and a glass of milk for each of us. After they disappear she says, "Mary Alice, why don't you show Alec the picture of your Uncle Quentin?"

Mary Alice takes me into the den, which is obviously her father's room. Two of the walls are paneled, and a big stone fireplace dominates one end. A mule deer's head stares at me with glass eyes from over the mantle. I count the points, six on each antler, and whistle approvingly. Two trophies on the mantle flank the head. Each shows a man aiming a gun.

I indicate the trophies. "Your dad's?" I guess.

"Yes," she says. "Trap shooting. He got the deer too." She goes to a group of photos on the wall and carefully takes one down. She has to stand on tiptoe to reach it. She places it on a glass-top table by a leather sofa and motions for me to come over and take a look.

The photograph has funny brownish tint—called sepia, I later learn. Three men in strange uniforms stand in front of a World War One-era biplane. The one in the middle has eyes like Mary Alice. I point to him and say, "I'll bet that one's your uncle."

"Yes. That's Uncle Quentin. He was already fourteen when Dad was born. He was killed just a couple of days after this was taken." She blinks rapidly, as if trying to hold back tears. "He was only twenty when he died."

I wonder why she gets so worked up over an uncle she never meets. He must die twenty-five years before she is even born "Do you know who the other two are?" I ask quickly.

"The one on the left is Victor Chapman. The one on the right is Raoul Lufbery. He was an ace. They were all killed."

"Do you know what the plane is?"

"A French Nieuport 17. Those are French uniforms too. They were all in the Lafayette Escadrille. It was formed before America even entered the war."

I'm impressed. Girls aren't supposed to know anything about military history. "Where did you learn all that?" I ask her.

"Dad used to tell Ron and Rob stories about him at night when I was supposed to be in bed. But I'd hide on the stairs and listen."

"Stairs?" I ask.

"In our old house down on the flats. We moved up here last year so we could pick up KPTV."

I follow her gaze across the room to the big console television set against the wall. The screen must be twenty-one inches. "Does it come in clear?" I ask.

"Just a little bit of snow sometimes," she replies. "Dad's going to put up a bigger antenna next month. That's supposed to clear it up." She sees the longing in my face and adds, "Mom says I'm not supposed to turn it on when I have company."

"Oh," is all I can say. In 1952 a mother's word is law.

After a couple seconds of embarrassed silence, she picks up the photo and tries to put it back on the wall. I take it from her and say, "Here. Let me get it." I'm almost five inches taller than she is, and I have longer arms. But as I reach up with it, my arm brushes against hers and a static electricity spark jumps between us. She gives a little squeak and I let go of the picture. I grab for it, juggle it at knee level and then drop it. But the carpet cushions the fall and nothing breaks. I pick it up and very carefully put it back in place.

"Sheesh!" I exclaim. "Talk about living up to my nickname! I'm sorry. Did I hurt you?"

"No. You just startled me. It's the carpet," she explains. "Ron zaps me all the time."

We are still standing very close. She looks up at me and asks, "Alec, why did you do it?"

"Put the picture back? I didn't think you could reach it."

"No. Why did you help me with the poem this morning?"

I'm about to shrug when I look into her big, spaniel-like eyes and decide, even though I'm talking to a girl, to tell the truth.

"Nicknames," I say.

A shadow seems to pass across her eyes. "What do you mean by that?"

"You have one that you don't like, and now I have one too, ever since the game with Crawford a couple weeks ago," I explain. "So I guess we have something in common."

"What do they call you?" she asks. We remain standing very close, and our voices barely rise above a whisper.

"Ol' Butterfingers, and it has nothing to do with the candy bar."

It sure doesn't. Even now I can close my eyes, look back in my mind and see that awful Thursday afternoon and that play that could make me a hero, but gets me branded instead.

We're playing Crawford, a school on the east end of town, in a game of single-platoon flag football. We wear red helmets with no face masks, shoulder pads and red jerseys with gold numbers that our mothers have sewn on so they can tell who is who out on the field. Crawford has green helmets and jerseys, but no numbers yet. Pants and shoes are whatever you want to wear.

I'm a single-wing quarterback on offense and a halfback in a seven-diamond defense. That might sound impressive, but a single-wing quarterback almost never touches the ball. I call signals, but I'm really just a glorified guard in the backfield. Any chance I have to touch the ball has to come on defense.

It's late in the fourth quarter, and it looks like the game will end in a scoreless tie. Most of them do. I have two or three flags to my credit. I break up a pass, field a couple of punts and return one for ten yards before being pushed out of bounds. Now I watch the Crawford punter drop back on fourth down to kick again.

He's left-footed. I watch him rock nervously up on his toes as he waits for the snap, and some inner voice tells me that he's going to shank it. So at the snap I run forward and slant to the right instead of dropping back. Sure enough, he pooches it off the side of his foot and it comes straight for me.

He couldn't lead me any better if he throws me a pass. I'm almost at full speed and there's nothing but open field ahead. Nobody can get me. We've never beaten Crawford for as long as I can remember, and here comes the win. All I have to do is haul it in and keep going. I see myself crossing the goal line and the crowd, all thirty of them, going wild.

I reach out to pull it in, and there's a sharp pain as the point catches the tip of my middle finger and bends it back.

I let out a yelp and stumble. The ball slides on through my grasp, bounces and rolls out of bounds. Next thing I know, I'm lying flat on my face and hammering the grass in rage and frustration.

Mr. Hunter, the sixth-grade teacher who coaches us, pulls me to my feet and tries to console me. "It's all right, Alec," he says. "We've got the ball and good field position. Get back in the huddle and call a fullback spinner on two."

We push it close, but time runs out before we can score. My finger is throbbing and beginning to swell, so Mr. Hunter splints it with a tongue-depressor and adhesive tape in the locker room after the game. "You jammed it," he tells me. "Be all right in a day or so." Then he looks at me quizzically. "How did you know he was going to shank that kick?"

I try to put it into words, but body language is a concept I won't understand for years yet. "It was just the way he was standing," I try to explain. "We almost got to him the time before. I-I could tell he was nervous, so I guessed he'd try to rush it and screw up."

"You were absolutely right. Good thinking!" He says that loud enough for the others to hear. Then he drops his voice and adds, "You know, Alec, sometimes you think a little *too* much, and that's probably why you missed the catch. I'll bet you were thinking about how far you'd go with it before you had it."

Then he sees the look on my face and pats me on the shoulder. "It was still a fine play," he assures me. "It just wasn't quite a great play. Don't let it get you down. There'll be other games and other chances."

But when you are ten, all mistakes are devastating and all defeats are total. I can only see myself as a worthless, butterfingered idiot. Apparently, so do some of my teammates. Crawford is the last game of the season, and I blow the chance to go out with a win.

The next morning I open my desk and find a piece of a Butterfinger bar on my math book. I can't play in the pickup basketball game at recess because of the finger, and at lunch my teammates give my spot at our table to a non-player, and I have to sit somewhere else. None of them talk to me. I manage to keep the tears back until I reach home.

"It's mean of them," Mom agrees, "but they'll get over it. In another week it'll all be forgotten."

"The coach was right," Dad chimes in. "It was a fine play. You were the only one who saw it coming. They're just jealous. Give 'em a few days, and they'll come to their senses."

But they won't and neither will I. They probably would accept an apology and take me back, but why should I apologize? I'd go back if they'd admit I saw it coming when they didn't, but they won't. So we all dig our heels in and the split grows wider.

On Monday I deliberately make for a different lunch table. Tuesday morning I find another Butterfinger piece on my math book and make a big production of walking up to Mrs. Foster's desk and dropping it in the wastebasket. Basketball tryouts are set for Wednesday after school. They take anybody who shows up, but I go home instead and tell Mom I won't be playing this year. She asks me if I've ever heard the expression about cutting off your nose to spite your face.

"What are you going to do after school?" she and Dad ask.

"I don't know," I say, and then I realize that answer isn't going to work. "I could go to the library or study and work on projects to get my grades better. (They're pretty good already, but Dad always has his you-could-do-a-little-better lecture ready whenever report cards come out.)

So I drop basketball, and the split becomes a canyon. Four or five years down the line I will read Mark Twain's *Pudd'nhead Wilson* and identify with the man whose life changes forever when he tells a simple joke that no one understands. That play probably takes five seconds from snap to shank to fumble, but it starts a chain of events that alters my life completely. For openers, instead of working on bringing the ball upcourt against a press, I am up on The Hill spilling my guts to a girl with eyes like those we will see later on in Keane paintings.

(Okay, you wonder, what's a Keane painting? In the 60's and 70's Margaret and Walter Keane will turn out hundreds of paintings of children and small animals with huge sad eyes. People buy them up by the thousands, but never keep them very long because those huge, hypnotic eyes drain you of emotion in a matter of days. Mary Alice is like that. Look straight into her big sad eyes and you do strange things, as I soon discover.)

"So that's why they call me Butterfinger," I conclude.

Mary Alice looks up at me and blushes. "You know what the other girls call me when they think I can't hear them?" I nod but say nothing. If it's going to be said, she'll have to say it. So she does. "Little Miss Peepants," she whispers.

Suddenly I realize how close we're standing. Did I take her hand or did she take mine? "It's not fair!" she murmurs. "It's been four years since I—did that. Why do they keep remembering?"

"Dad says they'll forget the fumble the next time I catch one cleanly, but I don't think so. I'm always going to be the guy who dropped the sure touchdown."

"And I'll always be the girl who wet her pants in class."

Well, at least we have self-pity in common, and that's a powerful force when you're ten and suddenly become aware of how mean people can be. In other parts of the world, places with names we must memorize for geography quizzes, children starve or die from diseases we're protected from by a simple vaccination. We hold hands in a snug, carpeted room and bewail the unfairness of life with mouths still speckled with cookie crumbs.

"I promise I'll never call you that," I say as I take her other hand and pull her closer.

"And I'll never call you Butterfinger," she replies. "From now on, I won't even eat 'em."

Before I realize what I'm doing, I bend down and kiss her. As our lips touch, we feel the cookie crumbs. We break apart, somewhat embarrassed, and wipe our mouths. Then she reaches up and kisses me.

This is my first intimate contact with a girl since back in kindergarten, when Sandy Evans and I get caught playing I'll-show-you-mine-if-you'll-show-me-yours out behind her dad's garage. I'm wondering what to do next when Mrs. Patterson makes a sudden noise back in the kitchen. We break apart again, look around guiltily, and the magic moment passes and is gone forever.

"Alec, Ron and Rob are going to be home in a few minutes," Mrs. Patterson says as she appears in the doorway. "You might want to be on your way before then. They're great ones for teasing, especially if they see you kissing their sister."

I turn red again and Mary Alice goes pale. If this gets back to the girls at school, we'll be in all their jump-rope rhymes at recess. I remember them chanting the one that begins, *Two little lovebirds, sitting in a tree, k-i-s-s-i-n-g!*

Why did I ever offer to help her recite?

"I won't tell them," Mary Alice's mother reassures us. "Take some more cookies with you, Alec. You seem to be a nice boy. Just remember to check behind you. Girls usually close their eyes when they kiss someone. That's why you two didn't see me."

For some reason she sounds like Mr. Hunter saying, "It was a fine play. It just wasn't quite a great play."

****

But a pale November sun finally pokes through the overcast as I climb back on my bike for the ride home. It's downhill, then flat, and I tell myself I can probably coast almost all the way. I brake a little at the first intersection.

Then I think what the heck, stick my feet up on the handlebars and let the old Columbia roll.

Hey! I'm feeling good again. I do a good deed, kiss a girl and like it and learn something about the Lafayette Escadrille. I have a pocketful of cookies and the wind blowing my hair back as I speed down The Hill. I wonder if the rush of air that I feel on my bike is like what Escadrille pilots feel in their open cockpits.

At the bottom I coast for another block, then put my feet back on the pedals and start to slow down. It's a good thing I do, because he seems to come from nowhere.

Another bike appears suddenly from a driveway behind a parked car. I slam my feet back on the pedals to lock the brake, burn a nickel's worth of rubber off my rear tire and nearly spill myself as I skid wildly to the left. He goes hard right as I shoot past, and we miss each other by inches. But he turns too sharply and falls over on his left side just after I pass him.

"Jeez Lou-*eeze*!" I hear him yell as I pull out of the skid and fight to keep my own balance. "Think you're the Green Hornet or something?" he snarls when I come back to see if he's okay.

"Didn't your mom ever teach you to look both ways before you go out in the street?" I snap back. Then I see he's hurting, so I soften my tone. "Are you all right?"

"My wrist hurts like hell. Don't think it's broken, though." He pulls himself to his feet and picks up his bike, which has a canvas newspaper bag over the handlebars. Six papers, folded into triangles, lie scattered on the street. I jump off my own bike and pick them up as he rubs his wrist and examines the back of his left hand, which is scraped raw.

"Good thing it's your left and not your right," I comment.

"I'm left-handed," he answers. He looks to be a couple of years older than I am, probably in junior high. I've never seen him before.

"Oh." I make another quick decision. "Can I help you finish up? Looks like you just have a few left."

He hands me two papers and points to two houses across the street. "1560 and 1520," he instructs me. "Just toss 'em on the porch."

So I help him finish his route, and my life takes off in yet another new direction. A paper boy? Why not? I don't think anyone at Cozine delivers papers. We'd probably consider it a blue-collar, poor-kid's job, if we thought in those terms. But it might be a way to get out of picking strawberries and beans in the summer.

It's a ritual that most Morrisonville kids begin when they finish fourth grade. Strawberry picking starts right after school lets out for the summer, and pole beans take us right up to Labor Day. In 1952 Mexican farmworkers rarely come north of California. The migrant families in our area are mostly dust-bowl refugees. We refer to them as Okies or Joads (after the family in Steinbeck's *The Grapes of Wrath*). There really aren't enough of them, so the town kids are expected to help out—even Pete and Sam Cloninger, whose dad is president of the local bank and buys a new Lincoln every two years.

This past summer I pick on Tuesdays and Thursdays. For a couple of days it's almost fun. Then it becomes plain, hard work. Kids my size earn maybe a dollar a day. That's way more than my allowance, but I'm soon wondering if it's worth it. And then one Tuesday in August, while I'm out in the fields, my dog gets run over and killed.

But next summer it will be Mondays, Wednesdays and Fridays, and then five days a week until I'm sixteen. It's supposed to teach us all about hard work and the value of a dollar. Maybe it does, but I still hate it and will try just about anything to get out of it.

Of course I would want the afternoon *Oregon Journal*. Getting up at five every morning to deliver *The Oregonian* would be too much like picking berries and beans. The *Journal* has a morning delivery on Sundays, but once a week would be okay. So, as we finish the route together, I ask if I could get a job with the *Journal*.

He gives me a critical once-over. "Don't think you're old enough," he finally says. "J. P. wants you to be at least twelve."

For a moment my hopes are dashed. Then I think—wait a minute! My birthday is December 31. I can approach this J. P., whoever he is, right after New Years and tell him I'll be twelve later in the year. That wouldn't technically be a lie. So I tell the kid, "That's okay. I've got a birthday coming up." I just don't say which one.

"All right. After your birthday, come down and see J. P. Harrington. He's the boss."

"Where?" I ask.

"Benny's. You know where it is?" I nod and he continues. "Could be a couple of routes might come up in the spring. Two of the guys'll turn sixteen then. That's when they usually quit."

We finish the route and I head on home, unaware that my life has just taken another big lurch and will never quite be the same again.

Chapter Two: The Gift

We move forward to New Year's Eve and my eleventh birthday, with a couple of stops along the way. The first is any Sunday evening at seven. The dinner dishes are dried and put away, the comics in the *Journal* and *Oregonian*—we take both—well -read, sports pages checked to see how Oregon State and Linfield do (generally, not well), and now I'm curled up in front of our big old Philco console radio, with the dial set to KOIN, waiting for those thirteen eerily-whistled notes that announce my favorite program in all the world.

S-i-g-n-a-l! Signal! Signal gas-o-line!

I sing the tune silently as I watch the radio with my eyes closed and see in my mind a lone figure beneath a street lamp. Those thirteen notes cover two octaves, and I never can whistle them cleanly like the man under the light. (I'm very chagrined when I learn later on that a woman actually does the whistling.) But I can do the opening lines, and I recite them along with Bill Forman, my spiritual buddy and a man whom I will never meet.

"I am the Whistler, and I know many things, for I walk by night..."

The Whistler is cool, a term just coming into vogue in 1952. I suppose it means different things to different people, but to me it signifies power and freedom.

"I know many strange tales hidden in the hearts of men and women who have stepped into the shadows..."

Unlike his counterpart and rival, the Shadow, the Whistler never appears in any of the stories he introduces. He watches and makes ironic comments as the characters plot the perfect crime (usually murder) and always, *always* trip over some petty little detail they've overlooked. Then, with a last wry quip from the Whistler, I picture the evildoers marched off to trial, judgment and eventual execution—because that's what happens to murderers in 1952.

"Yes, I know the nameless terrors of which they dare not speak!"

"Just like the fly on the wall, isn't he?" says Dad, who always listens with me. Mom worries that the program will give me nightmares, but Dad and I scoff at the idea. "It's no more violent than *Hopalong Cassidy,* or *The Lone Ranger* or *The Cisco Kid,*" Dad assures her. "And it's certainly a lot less violent than *Gangbusters*. Besides, it teaches a good lesson. Crime doesn't pay. You can't get away with it."

I will come to question that later on, but in the late autumn of 1952 I'm still a believer. I picture God as a progressive Republican who nonetheless loves Democrats and pities their well-meaning foolishness—sort of a huge General Eisenhower with white hair and a long, flowing beard. To me America is an endless series of Morrisonvilles with an infinite number of schools like Cozine and countless fifth-graders like myself—well-clothed and fed (for the most part), polite and respectful (usually) and white (of course).

There are no racial minorities to put down in the Morrisonville of 1952, so we pick on the Okies and Joads from the labor camp instead. But we are very careful about how we do it, having learned a rather painful lesson back in the third grade.

Let's pause again and take a look at Davey Scroggins, a second or maybe third-generation Okie migrant whose father or grandfather lost the family farm during the dust bowl days of the 30's. I meet him in the third grade. Joads, white trash—

words our parents can use, but we're not supposed to. Davey and the other migrant kids live at the labor camp, closer to the tiny town of Whiteson, but they're bussed to Cozine because we're a big new school with room enough to take them in.

We take them in, but not all that willingly. They're *different*. Their clothes are worn and patched and don't always fit well. Some of those kids don't smell very good. They bring their lunches in paper sacks instead of buying hot lunch at school. And they still talk with a Southern Plains twang that sounds alien to our Pacific Northwest ears.

Poor Davey has a mouth, nose and two jug ears that are way too big for his face. His hair looks like a crosseyed barber with a bad hangover tries to cut it and gives up halfway through the job. (We learn later that's pretty close to what happens.) He reminds us of Denny Dimwit in the Winnie Winkle comic strip in *The Oregonian*, so we take to calling him Davey Dimwit. We're careful not to let the teacher hear us, though.

But one fateful morning in the spring of 1951, Davey shows up with his head shaved into a rough mohawk and two big bandages covering part of his baldness. As luck would have it, our teacher, Mrs. Chivington, is out of the room, and the sight is just too much for us. Twenty-six eight and nine-year-olds begin to hoot and point and caper like a pack of baboons. Three of the girls and I hold back.

I allow myself one good chuckle, then retreat to my desk and sit quietly. Not because I'm a model of virtue—an inner voice warns me that Mrs. Chivington will walk in at any moment, and things are really going to hit the fan when she does.

A girl named Helen from the camp puts her head down on her desk and cries. Janet Tabor, the tallest kid in the class and my enemy (though I'm not sure why), sits silently beside me, while Peggy Miller, whose desk is next to the hullabaloo, retreats across the room to the globe and begins diligently studying Asia while the pandemonium continues.

Then Mrs. Chivington walks in.

She is a tiny woman, already in her sixties, who reminds me a little of Granny in the Tweety and Sylvester cartoons. She doesn't get angry often, but when she does, she seems to swell like a thundercloud getting ready to break loose.

Right at that moment she looks like she's seven feet tall.

Davey crouches in a corner, crying and holding his hands over his mutilated scalp as if trying to ward off blows, though no one actually tries to hit him. His tormentors are too busy hooting and pointing to notice Mrs. Chivington until she reaches her desk, pulls out a wooden ruler and brings it down on her desktop so hard that it snaps in two. Everyone freezes, and there is total silence for about three seconds. Even Davey stops blubbering.

"In your seats!" she commands. "NOW!"

Everyone but Davey races for their desks. He still crouches with his hands over his head. Mrs. Chivington helps him up, gives him a hug and tells him to wait outside. Then she turns her attention to us.

"In all my years of teaching," she begins, "I have never broken a ruler until now. This is the most disgraceful performance I have ever seen! Apparently I cannot leave you alone for three minutes without chaos, *utter chaos,* breaking out!" She pauses to draw a deep breath, slings the broken ruler into the wastebasket and continues.

"I was down in the office talking with a policeman about Davey. Do you know why he's so badly marked up? His two oldest brothers came home drunk last night, held him down and shaved his head with a razor—a *straight* razor! There are five stitches under one bandage and three under the other. One brother actually told Davey he'd cut his ear off if he tried to fight! Well, at least they're both in jail now, but how would *you* like to go through something like that and then have to come to school and face a pack of gibbering hyenas? Because that's what you're all acting like—a pack of gibbering hyenas!"

I'm an only child, so I can't really imagine what brothers like that are like. They must be pretty horrible. I want to protest that I'm not part of that pack, but that same voice warns me not to speak up now. Beside me Janet is quivering with fear or rage or maybe both. The other girls put on their I'm-so-sorry-that-I'm-going-to-cry faces, but Mrs. Chivington isn't buying a bit of it.

"To begin with, no recess for a week. *To begin with!*" She lets this sink in while she pulls another ruler from her desk. "I'd use this on each one of you," she continues, "but it's my last ruler and I don't want to break it. Or I might send you down one at a time to have the principal deal with you."

Now the girls are getting set to cry in earnest. The boys are looking very uncomfortable, and my breakfast is dancing the polka in my stomach. A session with the principal in 1951 means a lot more than a chewing out. Mr. McDougall keeps a paddle in his office and is known to use it—hard and often! Just when we think it can't get any worse, she tops it.

"And of course I will call your parents and let them know exactly what has happened."

Now the polka in my stomach becomes a jitterbug. Every fall on the first day of school Dad warns me that if I ever get a licking at school, he'll find out how many licks they give me and double it when I get home. I don't know if he means it or not, since I've always been too scared to tempt fate. But unless I do some mighty fast talking, I may soon find out.

I steal a quick glance at Janet, and she looks like she gets the same warning. In fact, judging by the faces around me, just about everyone does. Hey, it's a good thing Mary Alice is in the other room. She'd probably be piddling her drawers again.

Then Mrs Chivington says that magic word, "*However…*" and hope begins to flicker.

"However, I think I will let Davey decide your fate." She replaces the ruler and marches from the room. She is gone for just a few seconds, though it seems to us like an hour. Then she returns with Davey and places him in front of us.

"Davey, should I have the principal deal with them?" she asks.

We hold all our breath while he ponders the question.

"No, Ma'am," he finally answers. "It's okay. They didn't mean nothin' bad."

"And what about recess?"

Davey is far from being the brightest bulb in the chandelier, but this time he gets it right. I figure out later that Mrs Chivington coaches him, but just then he comes across as an Einstein. "Please let 'em come out, Ma'am. I won't have nobody to play with." None of us ever play with him, but we all take a solemn, silent vow that we will from now on.

Mrs. Chivington works us like field hands for the next hour. Finally the buzzer goes for morning recess. "Remember!" she says as we stand up. "You get to go out because of Davey. I expect you all to stick up for him." She looks straight at John Folsom and Larry Dale, by far the toughest twosome in the third grade. "You are not to *start* a fight," she warns them, "but if you have to use your hands to protect Davey—so be it."

John and Larry smile, and I know Davey is safe. The bigger kids have recess later, and no one our size is going to tangle with those two. But as we line up, Mrs. Chivington says, "Helen, Janet, Peggy and Alec—stay here. I want to talk with you for a minute."

She makes us wait until the others are well down the hall. Then she says, "I know you four were not part of that mob. Helen, Davey is your cousin, isn't he?"

"Yes'm. Our moms are sisters."

Mrs. Chivington dismisses her, and she runs out to join the others. "As for you three," she tells us, "you almost did a noble deed. You came oh so close, but you failed."

Before I can speak up, Janet blurts, "But Mrs. Chivington! We didn't tease him!"

"That's true, Janet. But did you try to stop the others?"

"Stop them? How could we?"

"You could have tried. Do you all go to Sunday School? Do you know who Pontius Pilate was?"

I'm a Presbyterian, and I learn that Peggy's a Baptist and Janet's a Methodist. Yeah, I kind of remember who Pilate is, but why is Mrs. Chivington bringing him up here?

"He's the man who washed his hands in front of the crowd?" Miller guesses.

Mrs. Chivington nods. "Yes. He knew what the mob wanted was wrong. He had the authority to stop them, but he was afraid to use it. So he said, 'Don't blame me. I'm not a part of it.' Then he washed his hands and turned away. And that's what you three did. Evil succeeds when good people do nothing." She says that very slowly and then repeats it. "You three are good people, but you did nothing. Don't let that happen again."

I learn much later that she is paraphrasing an English jurist named Edmund Burke, but that seven-word sentence about evil succeeding burrows down through my consciousness and buries itself in my memory. I will recall it and act on it many times in later years, and it will get me into lots of trouble.

****

Now at last we come to my birthday. I am born, so they tell me, on December 31, 1941, at 11:47 p.m. Mom always regrets that I just miss the prize for First Baby of the New Year, but Dad calls me his little thirteen-minute deduction, since he gets to claim me on his 1941 income tax, even though I'm only here for thirteen minutes of it. Dad's an accountant, and things like that mean a lot to him.

Since it's New Year's Eve as well as my birthday, I get to stay up past midnight and sleep in the next morning. But I have to wait until 11:47 p.m. to open my presents. My birthday is just far enough from Christmas to guarantee me separate gifts. I get five—one each from Mom and Dad, one from Grandma and Grandpa Fullerton over in Salem, one from my Grandma Lewis back in Iowa and one from Aunt Emma Snyder up in Portland.

We always go to Grandma and Grandpa Fullerton's for Christmas, and Aunt Emma Snyder comes down to spend New Year's with us. She is a widow like Grandma Lewis, whom I have never met. I love Grandma Lewis out of a sense of duty—she is my dad's mother, after all, and she always remembers my birthday—but Aunt Emma Snyder is special. She's nothing like Dorothy's Auntie Em in *The Wizard of Oz*. My Aunt Emma is the black sheep that every family has, every parent fears and every child loves.

Aunt Emma Snyder is an ex-communist. Not some namby-pamby, cocktail party, intellectual pinko. Aunt Emma is (or was) the genuine article. Back in the 20's and 30's she marches, pickets, writes nasty articles for the *Daily Worker* and actually spends time in jail for her beliefs. In 1937 she and her husband run off to Spain to fight in the Abraham Lincoln Brigade during the Spanish Civil War. He gets himself killed over there, and she just barely makes it out.

But when Stalin signs a pact with Hitler in 1939 and thus starts World War II in Europe, Aunt Emma becomes so disillusioned with communism that she drops it and becomes a Christian. Of course, she can no more be a quiet, every-other-Sunday Presbyterian like us than she could be a mere cocktail-party socialist. She becomes a pastor and evangelist instead, taking on the twin evils of strong drink and socialism. By 1952 she has her own church and radio show, each with a small but very devoted following. Dad says she reminds him of Aimee Semple McPherson.

"Who's that?" I ask.

"A lady much older than I, and not nearly as wise in the ways of the world," Aunt Emma says.

But she has been a part of my birthday for as long as I can remember. She visits us every New year's Eve to celebrate Alec's Day, as she calls it, and have Dad check over her accounts before tax time. Then, after the books are balanced, she gets roaring drunk and her old commie radical self resurfaces for one evening.

"But isn't drinking what you preach against?" I always ask her.

"You need a little sinfulness every now and then to remind you what virtue is," she replies. "I'm a good Christian 364 days a year—365 this year, since it's leap year—which is more than most people can say. But Alec, even saints need to go on a little rampage once in a while."

She's rampaging right along when I head upstairs to take a bath and get my pajamas on, and I can hear her at the piano as I come back down. Aunt Emma is an enthusiastic if not overly talented player, and she does have a strong contralto voice. I recognize the song, *The Internationale,* which Aunt Emma can sing in four different languages. Tonight she's warbling in French, which means she's already pretty well smashed.

"Un de ces matins, disparaissent
Le soleil brillera toujours!"

She catches sight of me on the stairs and cries, "Alec! Join me in the chorus! Do remember from last year?"

Well, I am a quick study, as actors say, and I can retain something if there's a reason to. I join her at the piano and we belt out the chorus together.

"C'est la lutte finale:
Groupons nous et demain.
L'Internationale sera la genre humain!"

"God! I hope the neighbors don't understand French!" Dad mutters as we harmonize it a second time. I never forget the words I sing, but I never get around to learning what they mean.

Mom brings an end to the concert by reminding me it's time to open my presents. There's a book or two—probably the Hardy Boys or one of Jim Kjelgaard's dog stories. Dad gives me a model airplane kit that I request—a French World War I Nieuport 17. Aunt Emma holds hers back until I open the other four.

It feels like another book, but it's bigger and heavier. I tear the wrapping off and discover that it is a book, with a fancy leather cover, but no text. Is it a scrapbook, a diary or what?

"It's a journal," Aunt Emma explains when I give her a puzzled look. "Fitting, don't you think? Your father tells me you want to become a *Journal* delivery boy."

"What do I do with it?" I ask.

"You make a record of this your twelfth year," Aunt Emma says. "There are places for you to write about what happens to you every day and places for you to paste in articles from the papers. You read them now, don't you?"

"Just the funnies and the sports page," I admit.

"Oh, you'll need to read more than that!" she exclaims.

"Why?" I catch the frown on Mom's face and backtrack quickly. "I mean, it's very nice of you to give me this, but..." Aunt Emma's gift seems more like a gigantic homework assignment than a present.

"It's a chance for you to create your own book, Alec," Aunt Emma explains. "Years from now you can read it and remember what your twelfth year was like." She slips into her evangelist's voice. "A chronicle of a year in a life! A precious memory to keep forever! Promise me you will try it!"

I guess I must still look doubtful, because she sighs and says, "I guess I shall have to resort to bribery. You still miss Laddyboy, don't you?"

That hits a nerve. Laddieboy is, make that *was*, my dog—a cocker spaniel with big brown eyes. A log truck smashes him flat on a Thursday in August while I'm out picking beans. Dad has him buried before I get home and won't tell me where, so I never get the chance to say goodbye.

But all through the fall I run across reminders of him—a ball we play fetch with, a slipper he chews. I throw them in the trash and try to blot his image out of my mind, but in my dreams he keeps coming back, running and playing and looking at me with those big brown spaniel eyes like—

I guess I close my own eyes because they pop open again when the image hits me. Mary Alice has eyes like that, big and brown and full of emotion like a spaniel's. And being the shortest girl in the class, she looks up at me with almost the same expression and tilt of the head. Is that why I kiss her—because she reminds me of my dog?

Aunt Emma takes another swallow of vodka and orange juice and proceeds with her bribe. "Well, one of my flock has a beautiful purebred springer spaniel bitch—"

Dad gives an embarrassed cough and Aunt Emma turns on him. "Henry, that *is* the proper term for a female dog!" Then she takes another swallow and turns back to me. "Mind you, Alec, if I ever hear you call a *human* female that, I'll box your ears good and proper! Use your words like you use your tools—for the purposes for which they're designed. Saying something like that to a girl is not only hurtful, it's ridiculous like driving a nail with a saw or cutting a board with a hammer."

"Aunt Emma, I've never said anything like that!" I protest, although I admit silently that I've been tempted a few times, especially with Janet Tabor.

"Of course you haven't, my dear. It's just that words—" She looks at her drink and shakes her head. "Oh dear! I'm getting fuzzy already. Well, here's the offer. The *dog*, if you insist on being a prude, Henry, is still a puppy herself right now, but she'll be ready to breed by summer. I'll come back for a visit on the Fourth of July. If you've done a good job and promise to continue, you'll get a beautiful springer spaniel pup for your twelfth birthday."

I'm trapped. Getting permission to try delivering papers has used up all my credits with Mom and Dad and left me with no room to weasel out of anything else. "Okay," I agree.

The radio begins the countdown of the last seconds of 1952. Aunt Emma refills her glass, while Mom and Dad pour champagne for themselves. Then, for the first time, they pour a small glass for me. "For our big boy!" Mom says as she hands it to me.

"Happy New Year!" Dad cries as the clock strikes twelve and we hear Guy Lombardo's band break into *Auld Lang Syne*.

My drink is so small that I try to take it all in one swallow like Aunt Emma. The result is a tremendous burp, and the bubbles seem ready to run out my nose. Aunt Emma drops her empty glass and hugs me. "Alec!" she cries as she looks at me with eyes starting to go glassy. "This is going to be a year you will never forget! I just know it!"

None of us have any idea how right she is. Me least of all.

Chapter Three: Beginning

New Year's Day, 1953, falls on a Thursday. Mom and Dad have let me sleep in, so it's after nine o'clock by the time I come down to breakfast. I can hear Mom working in the kitchen, but the first person I see is Aunt Emma, sprawled in Dad's easy chair in front of the fire with a coffee cup in her hand. She does not look up when I wish her a Happy New Year.

"'Wine is a mocker, strong drink is raging; and whosoever is deceived thereby is not wise.' That's from Proverbs, Alec. Chapter twenty. First verse."

"I remember. You recited it last year."

"And I'll recite it next year too, if I live that long."

I want to ask her why she does it, if it makes her feel so bad, but I can tell she's in no condition for personal questions. So instead I ask her, "Did you really mean what you said last night, about getting me the dog if I do the journal?"

She finally looks up at me and manages a weak smile. "Absolutely," she replies. "Drunk or sober, I keep my word. But you have to do your part too."

"I will. You said you'd help me get started. Dad's probably reading *The Oregonian* now, but maybe—"

"Let's wait for the *Journal* this afternoon. I'll need at least three cups of coffee and two more aspirin before I'll be of any help."

So Dad and I turn on the radio and listen to the bowl games. There are only five that count for anything in 1953, and they are all played on New Year's Day. I paste the results in my journal the next day. Southern California beats Wisconsin in the Rose Bowl. Texas over Tennessee in the Cotton Bowl. Georgia Tech whips Mississippi in the Sugar Bowl. Alabama clobbers Syracuse in the Orange Bowl, and Florida edges Tulsa in the Gator Bowl. (There's also a Rice Bowl, Salad Bowl and Spaghetti Bowl played by American armed forces units stationed abroad.)

The *Oregon Journal* lands on the front porch during halftime at the Rose Bowl. Aunt Emma, feeling better now, spreads it out and we scan the front page together. The main headline reads, "Purcell Appointed Chief of Police." We cut it out and I paste it on a page reserved for the week's main headlines. But we both agree it's not that important.

Aunt Emma skips over the war news and stories about Eisenhower's upcoming inauguration and points to a small item near the bottom of the front page. I read the simple heading—"Hillbilly Singer Dies."

"You think that's important?" I ask.

"Absolutely! You mean to say you've never heard of Hank Williams?"

I haven't, and even if I have, I wouldn't admit it. The term "country-western" doesn't exist in 1953. Hillbilly singers are cornball, strictly from hunger, as we say back then. Mom and Dad have a collection of Frankie Laine and Jo Stafford records they play at night when there's nothing good on the radio, and the bobbysoxers are swooning over Johnnie Ray. But fifth-grade boys in Morrisonville don't care very much for records, especially not hillbilly records by Okies who sound like they come from the labor camp.

So what do we care about? From April through September—baseball. In January—basketball, the war in Korea and comic books. A couple of my buddies have older brothers serving in Korea, and all my friends and I collect and swap comic books about the war—especially the jet aces like Blackhawk and Captain Steve Savage. It's strange to think that sad little Mary Alice is the niece of a combat pilot.

Comic books cost a dime down at the Smoke Shop on Third Street, and the Buster Brown comics are free at the shoe store. I have a mint-condition run of Buster Browns going back four years, but of course they all get thrown out when I leave home for college.

Yeah, I'm a great collector, but I don't hang on to things. My baseball card collection includes Mickey Mantle's rookie card, but I give the whole shebang to a neighbor kid when I start high school. The little snot-nose is smart enough to hang on to them and sells the collection years later for ten thousand dollars.

****

School doesn't start up again until Monday the 5th, but on Friday the stores are open again, and I'm heading down to Benny's to meet this mysterious J. P. Harrington, boss of the *Journal* delivery boys. I've ridden a few times over part of his route with Pat Rush, the boy I nearly knock over back in November, but I've never been to their headquarters or met any of the other carriers. I know where they hang out, though.

If you're a boy in Morrisonville in the 1950's, then you know Benny's Bike & Hobby Shop, way down at the east end of the Third Street business district, next to the old Southern Pacific depot. Benny rebuilds, fixes and sells bicycles, new and used. He also has one of the biggest selections of model railroad, model plane and model car kits in the state. There's a pop machine and candy and gum at the front counter.

The place has three sections—the front shop, where Mrs. Benson presides, then Benny's workshop, where rows of bikes in various stages of assembly wait to be worked on. At the back of the workshop a doorway leads to a small, bare room with a three-foot-high shelf running around three of its walls. Five days a week, between two and three in the afternoon, a truck from Portland drops off just over 700 copies of the *Oregon Journal* for the twelve paperboys who deliver them around the town.

On Saturdays the papers come in around eleven in the morning. On Sundays or holidays when Benny's is closed, they're dropped off at O'Dell's Flying-A Station down on Third and Ford.

It's not quite three on January 2nd when I wave to Mrs. Benson and walk back through Benny's workshop. "Hello, Alec," he calls without looking up. "Did your dad give you that model yet?"

"The World War I fighter? Yessir. He gave it to me for my birthday. I'm gonna have to get some tan and silver paint, though. It's plastic and the color is all wrong."

Benny sets down his tools and reaches for his crutches. Polio has left him crippled, but he can drag himself along pretty good with them. "I've got some stuff a kid brought back. Should still be good. Sell it to you cheap. Where'd you ever hear of a Nieuport 17?" he adds as he hauls himself to his feet. He has the arms and shoulders of a weightlifter. "Never had anyone ask for one of them before. They all want the F-86 or the F-90."

"Uh, a friend told me about it," I say as casually as I can. "But that's not the reason I came back here." I gesture toward the back room. "Is J. P. in there"

"Oh, sure. Just walk on in," Benny says. "They don't bite—much." He drops back on his chair and returns to work.

A single bare bulb in the ceiling throws an uneven light over the back room. Seven or eight boys fold or roll newspapers stacked in piles along the shelf. A stocky man with black-framed glasses, thinning hair and a salt-and-pepper mustache stuffs tobacco from a Prince Albert can into an old pipe as he jokes with one of the bigger boys. This has to be him, so I take a deep breath, walk up to him and say,

"Excuse me, Sir. Are you J. P. Harrington?"

"Yep," he answers. "What can I do for you?"

"I'd like to be a *Journal* delivery boy," I tell him.

He looks me over as he jams the pipe in his mouth, then digs a kitchen match from his shirt pocket and lights it with his thumbnail. "Would you now?" he says as he draws the flame down into the bowl. "Don't think you're big enough yet. How old are you?"

This is the line I've rehearsed since November. "I'm eleven right now, but I'll be twelve later this year."

"Uh-huh, and I suppose I'd better not ask how much later." He takes a puff and blows a cloud of smoke up at the ceiling. "Well, we don't have any routes open just now. Why don't you come back and see me when you're twelve?"

Dad has warned me that this would probably be his first response. After some initial reservations, he's become an eager supporter and coaches me on what to say if J. P. tries this line. So I put his coaching to use.

"Maybe not now, but you will have," I say. "Meanwhile I'm willing to ride with some of the guys and learn their routes. You could always use a substitute, couldn't you? Somebody might get sick or have to go somewhere."

J. P. pauses for another puff and more smoke drifts up toward the light bulb. "You may have a point there," he concedes. "And how much would you want to charge for this?"

"Nothing until I actually substitute. Then whatever you think is fair."

J. P. is silent for several seconds while the smoke curls up from his pipe. I can tell he's thinking it over, and that's a good sign. His face is pitted from some childhood ailment, and it reminds me of an old rock being slowly worn smooth again over time.

"You're still kind of small," he finally says.

"But I'll get bigger."

"Yep. You will do that." He removes the pipe and points the stem at me like a gun. "I've had boys like you show up in June or July, when the weather's nice and school is out. But you're the first one to come around in January. Are you willing to ride in the rain and the snow? Are you willing to get up at five o'clock on Sunday mornings?"

"Yes," I tell him.

"All right then. We'll see if you can stick it out through January. Any of you guys want to take along an assistant? He's working for free."

I expect Pat Rush to volunteer, but another boy speaks up first.

"Sure," he says casually. He's the biggest one of the bunch, almost six feet tall, with dark hair well greased and combed back in a ducktail. "What's your name, Kid?"

"Alec Lewis."

"Ken Scott." My hand disappears in his, but he's careful not to squeeze too hard. I'm suddenly aware of just how small I am. At school I'm a little over average height for my grade, but the smallest carrier here is probably a couple years older and three inches taller than I am. This is my first experience at being the new kid, the baby of the bunch, and it makes me feel awkward and nervous.

"Hey, Twerp! Look who's going to be joining us," Scott says as he turns me around and shows me off. I see Jill Benson, Benny's daughter, standing in the doorway. She has the run of the shop, including the *Journal* room. Very few girls come in to Benny's, even though he sells girls' as well as boys' bikes. None ever go back to the workroom, except for her.

"Fold the rest of your papers for a pepsi, Kenny," she says as she strolls over and gives Scott a casual hug, totally ignoring me. She's maybe eight, maybe nine, and about as much smaller than me as I am to the next smallest guy.

"Not today," Ken says. "I hafta show this new guy how to do triangles."

"He won't be any good. Let me do 'em."

"Are you kidding? Let me introduce Alec the Speed Demon. Give me one minute to teach him, and he'll be faster than you ever thought of being!"

Jill finally gives me a casual once-over and shakes her head. "Never happen," she says.

"You wanta race him? Then get your box."

Jill pulls a wooden box from under the counter and stands on it. This gives her an additional half a foot, so she now stands about even with me. Ken divides his remaining papers into two stacks, two other boys pulling their stacks aside to make room. All the while J. P. Harrington is filling our lungs with used pipe smoke. None of us mind it a bit.

"You right or left-handed?" Scott asks me.

"Right," I answer. "But how do I race someone when I don't even know what I'm doing?"

"I'll show you. It's easy." He turns the stacks so they're end on, fold to the left. "Take the bottom right corner, bring it up to the fold and crease it. Got that?"

"Sure," I say.

"Now take the top right, bring it down and make another triangle like this. Then grab it here, fold once, fold twice, flip it and stuff. Okay, let's see you do it."

My first attempt is a mess, and he makes me do it over. The second one isn't so bad. The third one is pretty good. "Do one more to even the stacks," Scott says, and I do.

"Okay. You've each got sixteen papers. First one done wins."

"Wait a minute!" Jill demands. "What does the winner get?"

"Well, I think I'll go get me a Hershey bar. Winner can have two pieces, loser gets one." Before either of us can object, he says, "Ready? Go!"

Jill jumps to a quick lead, but by the eighth paper I get the rhythm and start closing the gap. The other carriers gather to watch. Most of them root for Jill, but Pat and another boy are cheering for me. I think I can catch her if I really bust my tail, but maybe it's better to let her win. Just not by much. I'm starting the third fold on my last paper when she slaps her sixteenth onto the pile. I finish four seconds later.

Finally Jill speaks to me. Two words. "Hah! Beatcha!"

Ken saunters back with the candy bar, breaks off three pieces and hands two to Jill and one to me. "See?" she says as she wolfs them down. "Told you I'd win!" She turns to J. P., who is still puffing his pipe. "Didn't I?"

"Well," J. P. says as he removes the pipe and points the stem at Ken. "I'd say Scott was the winner. Wouldn't you, Alec?"

I grin ruefully, already catching on, but Jill demands, "What do you mean?"

"He got the rest of his papers folded in record time, and all it cost him was three pieces of a five-cent candy bar. That works out to about a penny and a half."

I develop a grudging respect for Ken Scott. That con job is as old as *Tom Sawyer* and probably older, but he snares us both in it. Hey, we're lucky we didn't wind up buying the candy for him.

Scott and I stuff the folded papers into a set of double bags, then haul them out into a January afternoon full of a cold drizzle that is just a couple of degrees too warm for snow. As we strap them to the carrier stand over his rear fender, I notice that he also has a front bag on the handlebars. "Why two bags?" I ask him.

"Thursdays and Sundays," he says. "The papers are too big to fold then. I've got sixty-five dailies and sixty-seven Sundays, plus two bulldogs."

"What's a bulldog?" I ask as we pedal down to Galloway Street and turn right.

"The early Sunday edition. You deliver it on Saturday, right along with the dailies It's just a Saturday paper with the Sunday comics and magazine."

"But why is it called a bulldog?"

Ken just shrugs. "Beats me," he says.

We begin Ken's route on Fourth and Galloway. At the first house he shows me how to throw a triangle-folded paper. "Don't just grab it in your fist," he says. "Lay your index finger along the crease like this. Then, when you throw, you're pointing your finger right at the target. You may be high or low, but you won't be off to the left or right." He lofts the paper from forty feet and lands it right on the doormat.

Most of the houses on Scott's route date from 1900 to 1930 and have big front porches. He lets me throw a few easy ones, but he won't trust me with a long shot or a small target. "Look," he says. "When you get home, fold up some old ones like I showed you and practice hitting your own porch. I pay for every paper that goes into this bag."

"You do?"

"Yeah. That's how it works. You don't get a salary. You buy each daily for somewhere between three and four cents, then you sell it for five. Sundays and bulldogs cost you ten cents, and you sell 'em for fifteen. You gotta collect from each customer at the first of the month."

"How long does that take?" I ask.

"I can get most of 'em in two or three days. Enough to pay off J. P. But some are a real pain in the ass—like that place over there."

"They won't pay you?"

"They do, eventually." He hands me three papers and gives me three numbers on down the street. "Get those and meet me back here. I'll show you what I mean."

By the time I get back, he's on the porch talking to some lady. All I can see of her is a head done up in curlers peeking around the edge of the door. Before I can get off my bike, she closes it and Ken trudges back down the steps.

"Oh dear!" he squeaks in a mocking falsetto. "Is it that time again already? My husband is at work and I don't have a single penny in the house. Can you come back tonight? Hah! Stupid old broad's giving herself a Richard Hudnut special and just doesn't want to be bothered. Hope it turns her hair green!"

"But you'll get it tonight, won't you?"

"Probably not. She'll say, 'Oh dear! Roger has gone to his lodge meeting, and I forgot to ask him to leave the money for you. Can you come back tomorrow?' This'll go on for three or four days. But let me be twenty minutes late getting her precious paper to her, and she'll call J. P. and raise hell, and I get a complaint slip!"

It's only when he goes to shove it back in the front bag that I notice Ken is holding something that looks like a stack of cards with aluminum covers and two binder rings holding them together.

"What's that?" I ask.

"The route book. It's got a year's worth of receipts for each customer. You tear 'em off each card and give 'em to the customers when they pay you." He flips it open to show me. "White cards are daily and Sunday, blue is daily only and orange is Sunday only. You get a dollar ninety-five for the whites, a dollar thirty for the blues and sixty-five cents for the orange. I'll take in about a hundred and thirty bucks this month. 'Course, I'll only get to keep about thirty."

"But that comes out to a dollar a day!" I say wonderingly. My allowance in 1953 is fifty cents a week.

"You won't get that much," Scott cautions me.

"Why not?"

"'Cause you won't get this route. John Madigan wants it, and he gets first dibs. I'm gonna quit in April, 'cause I'll be sixteen then. J. P.'s promised me a motor route as soon as I can get a license and a car. Then Madigan gets this route, and maybe you can get his."

"Where does his route go?"

"Right down Third Street to the park. Couple of apartments on Second. Then you get the library and take

Second down across the Star Mill Bridge and onto Rockwood Hill. It's not a big route. He's got maybe forty, forty-five customers—lotta move-ins and move-outs." He notices my look of disappointment and adds, "You start at the bottom, just like any other business."

Ken has me deliver about half the houses while he stops five more times to collect. His luck improves and he gets all five. "Let me give you a tip," he says after the fifth. "Carry a bunch of nickels for the daily and Sunday customers, but put 'em in a pocket where it's hard to get 'em out. About half the time they'll say, 'Oh, that's okay. Keep it.' It can add up to an extra dollar every month."

The street lights come on as we finish up and I head for home. I'm a little cold, a little damp, but happy. I have a light on my bike now, a Christmas present, but I don't use it unless I have to. The clouds are low and the treat of snow almost audible, as if the air is trying to whisper a warning. I run the bike up on our big front porch, but I don't lock it. I don't even own a lock. Bicycles are never stolen off front porches in 1953.

Well...*almost* never.

****

Dad is impressed with the way I can fold a triangle, but he's not so impressed with Ken Scott after I tell him about the contest and his tip about the nickels.

"That kid is just a little too clever for his own good," he says. "I'd feel better if you rode with someone closer to your own age."

"How come?" I ask. "I don't mind being conned by that contest. Anyway, he won't catch me with it again. And he's not really being dishonest about the nickel. He always gives it to 'em if they don't tell him to keep it."

"No, it's not what he does. It's the way he does it." Dad reaches in his pocket and begins jangling his ring of keys again. I know this means he wants to explain something important, and he's nervous about getting the words just right. I remember his birds-and-bees talk sounds like it's accompanied by a drummer on the cymbals.

"Alec, there's a big difference between being smart and being clever. A smart person uses his talents and skills to benefit people. A clever person uses them to take advantage of others. You can get away with that for a while, but eventually people will figure it out. I'd better tell you something about being a businessman, because that's what a paperboy is."

Dad sits back in his chair and jangles the keys once again. He always wears brown or gray suits with matching bow ties. "It's what folks expect when they hear the word 'accountant'," he explains when I ask him once why he always dresses the same way. "Now if I *really* wanted to look the part, I'd get some sleeve garters and a green eye shade."

"Don't you dare!" Mom tells him at this point, and they both laugh.

Mom is not laughing just now, but I can hear her humming a tune in the kitchen as she prepares dinner. She always hums and smiles for two or three days after Aunt Emma finally sobers up and leaves.

"If you're in business, any kind of business," Dad continues, "then you depend on your customers for survival. Nobody has to come to me. There are other accountants in town who are just as good. There's more than one doctor, more than one barber, more than one grocer, more than one clothing store, more than one movie theater. And there's more than one newspaper too. You're in competition with *The Oregonian* and the local paper. Granted, the *Morrisonville Register* only comes out twice a week, but it's still competition. Right?"

"Yeah. I guess so."

"It is. When you're in a business, you have to convince people that you have the best product and the best service.

If you don't, they'll go to someone else. That's why I'm glad your aunt gave you that journal. You need to know all you can about the paper you're delivering. Have you done anything on it today?"

"Not yet."

"Then why don't you get cracking on the front section here?" He hands it to me and picks up the sports page as I scan the main headline above the fold. *Wilson Boys Doom Upheld!* I cut the story out and scotch tape it onto a page. Then I read it over.

Two brothers named Turman and Utah Wilson are going to be hanged at midnight up in Washington for kidnapping and murdering a girl in Vancouver three years ago. Since Vancouver (Washington, not the one in Canada) is right across the Columbia River from Portland where the *Oregon Journal* is printed, the paper gives the story two full columns on the front page and more on the inside. The gist of it is that their appeals have run out, there will be no clemency from Governor Langlie, and it's all over but the wait for midnight.

I'm not sure if any of the other boys read the stories or even glance at the headlines when the papers come in. The *Oregon Journal* is just a product to be delivered, to be rolled or folded and stuffed into bags and then thrown onto porches as quickly as we can take them around the town. What people do with them after we deliver them is no concern of ours—as long as we get paid.

Mom's good mood continues after dinner. After Dad and I do the dishes, she hauls out the popper and her largest mixing bowls and pops a big batch of popcorn for us to eat while we listen to the radio. She even melts a big extra pat of butter for me. "I know you like a little popcorn with your butter," she teases. Then we adjourn to the living room and turn on the old Philco.

First comes one of my favorites, *The Cisco Kid*, on KPOJ. Next we switch to KEX for Mom's choice, *The Symphonette*.

Then we keep it on KEX for Dad's pick, a crime drama called *Your F.B.I.* I wonder what Mary Alice is watching in her house up on The Hill, so I pick up the paper to check. KPTV has *Abbot & Costello,* followed by *You asked for It* and *The Big Story*. Lucky dog!

After *Your F.B.I.* Dad switches the radio off, and he and Mom each pick up a book. That's my cue to go upstairs and get ready for bed. It's been a good day. I've learned to fold triangles, worked with Ken Scott and collected my first wage—one square of a Hershey bar. Mom serves up a great dinner, and I have a belly full of popcorn as well. Yes, it's been a very good day for me.

And, I reflect, a very bad one for the Wilson Brothers.

Chapter Four: First Weekend

A few words at this point about money. You might wonder why a boy of eleven is so eager to work a job seven days a week for somewhere between twenty and thirty dollars a month. Well, these are 1953 dollars, and I learn one thing about money very early on. It's not how much of it you make that counts. It's what you can get with it.

Ken's Hershey bar costs him a nickel, and so do most other candy bars. The big ones sell for a dime. Ice cream cones are five cents for a single scoop, ten cents for a double. Milkshakes and sundaes are a quarter. A big banana split will set you back thirty-five cents. On the rare occasions when Dad takes us down to the Palm Café for dinner, I always get the Palm Basket. That's a hamburger with everything, a big order of fries and a coke. It costs sixty cents.

The money is different too. Dimes, quarters and four-bit pieces are pure silver. Dollar bills are called silver certificates, and you can trade them at the bank for real silver dollars. (Grandpa Fullerton calls them cartwheels and adds that less than ten years before I was born people still carried gold coins in their pockets.)

I know Dad wants a new car. We bought our DeSoto used two years ago, and it's starting to act a little cranky. Most of the new 53's cost between two and three thousand dollars, depending on whether you want a Chevy or a Buick, a Studebaker or a Packard, a Nash or a Hudson. "Maybe in September when they drop the prices after the 54's come out, we might be able to afford a new 53," Dad says to Mom. "What kind would you fancy?" I am not consulted.

"Anything, as long as it has power steering and an automatic transmission," Mom says.

"And a radio!" I put in.

"Those things cost extra," Dad warns, "and I am *not* going to pay twenty-five hundred dollars for a car. Not on your life!"

But not everything is cheaper in 1953. I cut out and save an ad for a 21-inch black and white Admiral television set, which is the kind the Pattersons have. Five hundred and fifty-nine bucks for that thing! Even if Portland puts in the new channel they've been promising and we could pick up the signal, would we ever be able to afford something like that?

But I'm thinking about things I'll soon be able to afford as I pedal down to Benny's on Saturday morning. With a route of my own, I'll be able to get a candy bar or a pepsi whenever I want. I can get the latest Hardy Boys or Landmark books as soon as they come out and not have to put my name on a list at the library. Hey! I can even go down to the hardware store and pick out a sleek new knife to replace the ugly old cub scout jackknife that I carry in my front pocket every day.

(Of course how am I to know that the ugly old thing will become a collectable and sell for big dollars later on? I throw it out. *Dumb!*)

It snows during the night, but just a dusting, and it's melted by the time I get to Benny's. Mrs. Benson opens up at ten, and I'm the first one through the door. Benny is already at work in the back, but the *Journal* room is empty. "They'll be along in about forty minutes or so," Benny tells me. "Papers come in a little before eleven."

Jill is busy helping her mom stock the candy case. She makes a point of ignoring me, but when J. P. comes in she hugs him and laughs when he blows Prince Albert pipe smoke in her face. When Scott arrives, she hops on his back.

"Off, Twerp! You're gonna give me a hernia!" he protests, but he puts up with it for a minute before prying her off and setting her on the floor. "Go bother Alec. He's more your size."

"That drip? Uck!"

"Be nice to him, Twerp," Rush urges as he comes in. "You might even get him to kiss you."

"Double uck!" she cries and runs back to the front.

"I don't think she likes me," I tell J. P. This doesn't bother me, but I am a bit curious about it.

J. P. nods and blows a huge cloud of smoke at the ceiling. "She doesn't know what to make of you yet," he says. "See, she's been running around this place since she was five. You might call her our mascot. She's ridden on Ken's back almost four years now, but he's the last of the bunch that was here when she first came. Now he's going to be leaving soon, and you could be taking his place. You're only what? Two years older than she is?" He pauses to puff another cloud.

"She can't jump on your back. You're almost a classmate. Someday the new boy is going to be younger than she is. That's a fact she's going to have to get used to, and that's what she doesn't like, not you."

I'm still pondering this when the papers come in. The Saturday edition is the smallest of the week, only about half the pages of the other days. I fold a few for Ken and then stop to look at the main headline: *Wilsons Die: Lips Sealed*. Apparently both brothers refuse to say anything about the killing and maintain their innocence right to the end. Are they really guilty? It doesn't matter now—they're just as dead one way as the other.

I expect to ride with Scott again, but J. P. says, "No, go with Madigan this time. Is that okay, John?"

Madigan nods, but says nothing. I notice that he is the quietest one of the bunch. He's thirteen, just a little bigger than Rush, and has the look of someone who always has to be the bearer of bad news. I also notice he carries half of his papers flat. Today they fit easily into the single bag over his handlebars.

We catch the one house just east of the Southern Pacific tracks, then reverse and head west down Third Street. There are no malls or shopping centers in 1953. All businesses, except for a few gas stations, auto dealerships, small markets and cafes along the highway, are bunched down a five-block stretch of Third, from Galloway to Baker. Baker Street is also Highway 99W. There are no freeways in 1953 either.

Madigan leaves papers at both hotels, two of the three barber shops, Mom Jenkins' Popcorn Wagon, Stannard's Grocery and several other stores. At the Elks Club he simply tosses the paper on the porch, but at the Blue Moon he walks right in and beckons me to follow.

I've never been in a bar before, and I stand there blinking in the dim light. I see the bartender staring at me suspiciously, but before I can think of anything to say, Madigan tells him, "He's with me, learning the route." Then he turns and marches out, pulling me after him.

He also opens doors between shops and leads me up flights of dark stairs to small apartments that I never knew were there. I've always been aware of second and third-floor windows over some of the stores on Third Street, but it never occurs to me that people actually live up there. What kind of people are they?

After getting the police station and fire hall, we cross the highway at the town's only traffic light, head down to Adams Street and drop off a paper at the Morrisonville City Library. The library is at the south end of the city park. I live at the north end, about three blocks away.

Madigan gets three houses on the south side of Second Street behind the library, then leads me across the old Star

Mill Bridge that spans the creek flowing through the lower level of the park. Immediately beyond it we turn south, cross the Old White Bridge over Cozine Creek and head up onto Rockwood Hill.

Suburban sprawl is just getting started in Oregon in 1953. Second Street becomes Western Avenue and then a country road a couple hundred yards west of the Star Mill Bridge. There are two new streets west of the park. Then it's farmland. The Yamhill River forms the eastern boundary of the town. The curve of 99W pretty well marks the northern edge and the college the southern. The Hill, where the Pattersons live, is in the northwest corner. Rockwood Hill is in the southwest..

It's not even really a hill, just a small plateau cut off from the town by Cozine Creek and a couple of gullies. Apparently no one wants to farm it, so Morrisonville reluctantly draws it into the city limits and puts in streets and lighting. But only two of the streets are paved.

"Let me give you a piece of advice," Madigan says as he rolls a paper and stuffs it into an orange and green *Journal* tube under a mailbox. "If you get this route, wait till daylight before you come up here Sunday mornings, even in winter. And make sure you get it done before dark on weekdays. And watch your behind when you collect. There's some really weird people live up here."

"Like who?" I ask.

"Cap'n Andy, for one. You know him?"

"Oh, yeah! Does he take the paper? I didn't think he could read."

"Don't think he can either. Guess he just likes to play with 'em. J. P. gives me a couple of day-olds to give him if he asks for any. God knows what he does with 'em. He probably won't hurt you, but don't turn your back on him or get him riled."

Dad gives me the same advice. "I think his mother dropped him on his head when he was a baby," he tells me.

"Whatever the case, he's nuttier than a fruitcake. So don't mess with him. Just stay out of his way."

"But why isn't he locked up?" I ask Dad. "Why should I have to be on guard when he's the bad guy?"

"He's not really bad, just feeble-minded," Dad replies. "And he's not locked away because his uncle is a prominent lawyer and city councilman. Just leave the poor man alone, Alec, and he'll leave you alone."

Cap'n Andy is a short, squat, troll-like man who rides around town on an old black bicycle and always wears an ancient Salvation Army cap. His real name isn't Andy, but someone (so Dad tells me) nicknames him that after a character in *Showboat*. He stays with his mother, who's supposed to be almost as crazy as he is. Rockwood Hill would be a likely place for them to live.

One day last year two girls tease him as he rides past the library. Cap'n Andy leaps off his bike and chases them through the park yelling, "I'll rip yer drawers right off ya!" That brings the police, and Cap'n Andy is shipped off to the nuthouse in Salem for a couple of months. But his uncle is finally able to get him out. When he's due to be released, all the boys in my grade go into one classroom, the girls into another, and the fifth and sixth-grade teachers come in and talk to us.

Mr. Hunter just gives us the usual beware-of-strangers-with-candy lecture and then lets us out for early recess. But the girls are kept in nearly an hour, and they look pretty serious when we go back to our regular classrooms.

So now I find out Cap'n Andy lives on the route I might get. I decide not to share this information with Mom and Dad. At least, not yet.

****

Dad comes up to see me later that afternoon while I'm working on the Nieuport 17 in my room. The trick to making a really good-looking model is to paint the pieces before you glue them together. I've just finished the undercarriage and wheels. The wings and struts have dried and I've already applied the tricolor cockade decals, but there is one more delicate bit of business to finish.

Escadrille pilots carry a personal insignia on one side of the fuselage right beside the cockpit seat. This model has none, so I take the smallest brush I have, borrow Mom's magnifying glass from her sewing kit and paint a tiny Q P on the left side just in front of the squadron insignia. I'm finishing the P and blowing on it when Dad knocks once and comes in.

"Nice job," he says as he sits on the edge of my bed and examines the wings and struts. "Where do you plan to put it when you're finished?"

"Right there on top of the bookshelf. Or—" I suddenly find myself giving voice to a half-formed thought. "I might just, uh, give it to a friend."

Dad nods and jangles his ring of keys again. The ring stays in his pocket, but it fastens with a silver chain to one of his belt loops. It has fifteen keys. Dad tells me he knows exactly what six of them are for, has a pretty good idea about six more, but no clue about the last three. But he can never bring himself to throw a key away. "Never know when I might need it," he always says.

When he jangles them, he's nervous about something. Oh jeez! I think. Has he found out about Cap'n Andy living on Madigan's route? No, it's something else.

"The friend's name wouldn't happen to be Patterson, would it?" he asks quietly.

The surprise must show on my face because ne nods and gives me a half smile. "Bud Patterson spoke to me at the Elks Club the other night. He said his wife told him how she'd caught you and Mary Alice kissing." The smile broadens as he adds, "Not that there's anything wrong with that, providing the girl's agreeable."

"She was," I answer quickly.

"Well, that's good. I kind of hoped we'd have another year before I had to deal with this, but..." The smile disappears and he jangles the key ring again. "Son, Mary Alice is Bud Patterson's daughter."

"So?"

"You know what Bud Patterson does?"

"Yeah. He runs Patterson Pontiac & Cadilliac."

"He doesn't just run it," Dad tells me. "He owns it. And he owns interests in several other dealerships around the valley. I know because I work on his books. Bud Patterson is a very rich and ambitious man, and his main ambition is to get a lot richer. He's a man with plans, Son. Plans for himself and plans for his family. And I don't think they include us."

"What do you mean?" I'm beginning to catch Dad's drift, and I don't like it. "Are you saying we're not good enough for the Pattersons?"

"*I'm* not. As far as I'm concerned, we're their equals. But Bud Patterson doesn't think so, and Bud Patterson can hurt you if he sees you as a threat to his plans." I hear the jangle of keys again as Dad adds, "He can hurt all of us and smile while he's doing it."

For some reason the image of Davey and the other kids from the labor camp comes to mind. I remember how we treat them—being civil as long as they know their place and keep to it. Is this how it feels to be in their shoes?

"Dad!" I protest. "I kissed her once, almost two months ago. I haven't done it since. I haven't even held her hand!"

"I know," he says. "And I know you'd never be mean to her. But you don't figure in Bud Patterson's plans. Mary Alice will go to an exclusive college for a couple of years, then marry a football star turned medical student. His sons? I'll bet he has law school planned for one and a business degree for the other. He'll get them married to ex-cheerleaders, and then he can start planning his grandchildren's lives."

There's a bitterness in Dad's tone that I've never heard before. "All I'm saying to you, Alec, is this. Be very, very careful around Mary Alice. You're playing with fire when you cross the Pattersons. I know it doesn't seem fair, but then the world seldom is."

I listen to *The Lone Ranger* later that evening on KEX. Then at eight Dad turns the dial to KGW for the Oregon-Washington game. By halftime it's obvious that the Ducks are getting whipped, and I'm secretly glad because I'm an Oregon State fan, and the Ducks usually pound the Beavers. The final score is 76-60 in favor of the Huskies.

I give up on the game and go to bed early, since I have to get up at five tomorrow morning. But Dad's warning rankles me, and I have trouble falling asleep. I'm normally pretty cautious, but the one sure way to make me go after something is to tell me I'm not good enough to have it.

Mary Alice is not the prettiest girl in the class. In fact, except for those big sad eyes that remind me of Laddyboy (and the Keane paintings of a dozen or so years later), she's rather plain. And I'm not even that interested in girls yet. But I decide that night that I'm going to have Mary Alice Patterson for a girlfriend, whether her father likes it or not.

****

A town of about five thousand, back in the early 50's, between five and six on a Sunday morning in January. I suppose there are lonelier places, but I'd be hard put to come up with one just then. It snows during the night, but again only a dusting, and it's already melting under a cold drizzle that will coat the streets with ice if the temperature drops a couple of degrees before sunrise.

As I bump my bike down the front steps, I tell myself, *you could be back in bed now, warm and asleep like everyone should be before dawn on a winter morning. Instead you're going to ride through the cold and the wet and the dark—and for what? You won't get a cent for this morning's work.* But by the time I convince myself that it's stupid, it's too late. I'm out on the street and pedaling for O'Dell's Flying-A Station down on Third and Ford.

The silence is the eeriest part. I can't hear a car, a human voice, a dog barking or even a footstep. A single cat slinks across the street ahead of me, but I see no other sign of life. Every house is dark. The stores on Third and the apartments over them are dark as well. The busiest street in town lies empty and deserted in the pre-dawn drizzle.

Then I see lights at the Oregon Hotel on Third and Everett and, a block beyond, more lights at the Flying-A station and garage. J. P. has his old Chevy parked by one of the gas pumps. He seems surprised to see me.

"You're a real eager beaver, aren't you?" he says as I hop off my bike and look around for Ken or John. "Scott's already left, and Madigan isn't here yet. "You want to go with Rush this morning?"

"Sure," I tell him.

Pat ties his double bags to the carrier over my rear fender. "No sense in me carrying the whole load if you're coming along," he says as he stuffs the remaining papers into his front bag.

"Get back in an hour and I'll buy you both a cup of coffee or cocoa," J. P. calls as we ride away.

The drizzle has turned to snow again, but they're wet, heavy flakes that melt as soon as they hit the pavement. We begin on the highway just north of my house and work our way north and west. Pat gets two houses to my one, so he's soon taking papers from the double bags on my bike to stuff in the single on his.

"Wouldn't it be easier if I carried the single?" I ask him.

"It's tricky when the streets are slick—all that weight over your front wheel. Turn too hard and down you go. Remember when you almost creamed me?"

"Yeah. Lucky for you I missed. Lucky for me too, I think."

"How come for you?" he asks as we stop to shift papers.

"I never woulda thought of doing this. It's kinda fun."

"Fun? You're not gonna think it's fun when the weather really turns nasty. These papers have to be delivered every day, no matter what."

"Guess we're like the mailmen, right? 'Neither rain nor snow nor gloom of night…'"

"Uh-huh. You finish up by seven every Sunday and five every weekday or you don't work for J. P."

"Madigan won't finish that early this morning, will he?"

"He will with the town part. J. P. lets him wait for daylight to do Rockwood Hill, but he'd better be hauling his butt over the bridge as soon as the sun comes up."

Another thought crosses my mind. "Ever see Cap'n Andy on this route?"

"Old Looney Tunes? Not on Sundays. Once or twice during the week. I just tell him that Madigan has his papers and off he goes. That's the way to deal with him."

"I think I'll get Madigan's route when he gets Scott's."

"Well, we all gotta start somewhere," Rush says with a shrug.

The snow turns back to rain by the time we finish and head for O'Dells. I'm not sure what the time is, but it must be another hour until daylight. All the paper stacks are gone by the time we get back, and so is J. P.'s old Chevy. We see it parked down on Everett by the Oregon Hotel. J. P. sits at a counter inside the hotel coffee shop, nursing a cup while talking in low tones with the counterman. Four others, a couple and two singles, drink their coffee in booths along the front window. One picks halfheartedly at a sweet roll.

I glance at the clock on the wall behind the counter and ask Pat, "What are they doing down here at six-twenty on a Sunday morning? Why is this place even open?"

"Greyhound due in from Portland any minute now," Rush answers as we join J. P. at the counter. "Ever wonder who catches a bus at this hour on a Sunday morning or where they might be going?"

"You'd be surprised if you found out," J. P. says as he signals for two more cups. I start to ask for cocoa, then decide to go with coffee instead. For some reason J. P.'s signal tells me I'm now one of the crew, and if coffee is what they drink, then that's what I'll have to get used to—though I do lace it with plenty of sugar and cream.

"How'd it go?" J. P. asks as I try my first sip. I'm not sure if he's talking to Rush or to me, but I nod and mutter something about it being okay.

"He's all right," Rush adds. "No bitching, no gripes. Did what I told him."

"All right," J. P. says. "If you'll keep sticking it out, I'll put you first in line for the next route that comes up. Did Scott tell you he was going to quit in April?"

"Yes."

"Well, you won't get that one. Not yet. Madigan wants it and he has seniority. But you can have Madigan's route when he takes Scott's. It's a small one, but maybe you can build it up. Meanwhile, ride with as many of the guys as you can and check in with me every day, in case I need a sub."

Just then the bus pulls up in front. The four people by the window rise in unison, down the last of their coffee and drift silently toward the door. The couple quietly embrace a young man in a army uniform as he steps off the Greyhound. They all three disappear up the street, while the two singles give tickets to the driver and vanish inside the darkened bus. I wonder idly who they are and where they are going and where the young man who got off came from.

The driver drops off a package at the counter, takes a quick swallow of coffee and climbs back aboard his bus. I hear the hiss of air from his brakes as he closes the door. Then the bus is gone and we're alone. Three minutes later I can't remember what any of the people look like or recall a single word being spoken. It's like watching a movie with the sound turned off.

J. P. Notices me staring after the bus and nods. "Sunday mornings can be a little spooky sometimes," he says as he gives the counterman fifteen cents for the three coffees.

****

The Nieuport is finished when I head for bed soon after *The Whistler* ends. The weather report calls for more rain, but no snow, so there's no chance of school being postponed. "You didn't get your full nine hours last night, and school's going to roll around mighty tomorrow," Dad reassures me as I head up the stairs.

Yeah, Dad. As if I didn't already know.

Chapter Five: Gray Kaleidoscope

The rain! Oh Lord, the everlasting Western Oregon winter rain! We average almost half an inch a day for the entire month of January.

There's never a downpour. I never really get soaked, but I'm damp nearly every day from New Year's through March. The snow doesn't quite make it down to the valley floor, but we can see it up in the hills. Parents driving their kids down to school from Peavine Ridge arrive with an inch or two of crusty snow on their roofs each morning, but in Morrisonville we get rain. Oh sure, we do get one pretty good snowfall, but wouldn't you know? It comes on a Saturday and is gone by Monday—and what good is snow if it doesn't cancel school?

But as I cut out articles for my journal, I learn that other places have it lots worse. A British steamship capsizes and sinks in hurricane-force winds on January 31st, drowning 133 people. Two days later news reports estimate the total deaths in Europe from storms and floods to be well over 2000. Maybe we don't have it so bad after all.

I ride each day with Ken, Pat or John and then with three other boys, Pete Pietrowski, Dave Archer and Paul Reed. Pete's a little guy, not much bigger than I am, even though he's almost as old as Ken. We call Archer Dirty Dave, because he's supposed to have the biggest collection of dirty jokes in town. Paul Reed says he writes them down on note cards and keeps a file of them in a shoebox at the back of his closet.

Reed's another interesting character. In fact, all the *Journal* carriers seem to be a little quirky in one way or another. Paul lives with his grandparents, whom he calls Gams and Gump. One day, while we're working his route, I ask him about his mother and father. Paul just shrugs.

"I don't know," he tells me. "Gams always says she and Gump decided to skip them and go directly to me and Binky."

"Who's Binky?"

"My little sister. She's about your age. Doesn't go to your school, though."

"Yeah, but why is she called Binky? What's her real name?"

"I'm not sure. I think it's some long Italian-sounding thing. We just call her Binky." He looks at me somberly for a moment. "One thing you gotta understand about Gams and Gump. If they don't want to tell you something, there's no way in hell you're ever gonna find it out. I just figure someday, when they're good and ready, they'll tell me."

****

My career as a cub scout comes to an end when I start working for the *Journal*, although I do stick it out long enough to get my lion badge. They don't award that one anymore. It's red with a silver lion's head and probably worth something as a collectable. Needless to say, I lose it somewhere and don't get to cash in.

But on the afternoon of the last Sunday in January, Archer comes down with the flu, and J. P. stops by our house and asks me to sub his route, even though I've only ridden with Dave twice.

"How much do I get?" I ask a little hesitantly.

"Fifty cents a day, minus a nickel for every complaint," J. P. says. "Think you can handle it?"

Fifty cents? A whole week's allowance every day? You bet I can handle that!

J. P. gives me a list of Archer's customers in the order he delivers them. "Carry a pencil and check each one off every day until you know the route by heart," he advises. "I don't want to have to dock you, okay? You've been over most of his route, but the last house is his own, and that's over on First Street on Pietrowski's route."

"Why is that?" I ask.

"Each carrier always delivers his own house last. It's part of his route, no matter where it is. And every carrier's family has to take the paper. Your folks do, don't they?"

"Yep. Daily and Sunday."

"Good. When you take over Madigan's route, your own house will be the last stop."

Then he hands me Archer's double bags, and I tie them onto the carrier over my rear fender. "Take good care of 'em," he warns. "They're Dave's, but you can use 'em until he comes back. That could be two or three days or it could be a week or two. You never can tell with the flu."

He sees the next question in my eyes and digs two quarters from his pocket. "These will be yours after tomorrow, if you don't screw up," he explains. "I'll pay you for each day in cash and put it on Archer's bill, but you don't get your money until the following day. Is that all right?"

You bet it's all right! I have nothing against Dirty Dave, but I hope his flu lasts at least a week. Heck! Make that two weeks!

Of course, I want to carry Archer's bags to school with me, but Mom vetoes the idea because, naturally, it's raining again. "They'll soak clear through before school is over," she tells me. "You'd never be able to keep your papers dry." So I don't get to show them off—yet.

But on Monday the 26th I'm heading for Benny's as fast as I can make it home from school and change into the old jeans Mom makes me wear when I'm outside in the rain. There's a stack of fifty-two papers waiting for me, so I'll make right around a penny for each unless I mess up. But that's not going to happen, I tell myself. I'll use that list and check each house off until I know that route, backwards, forwards and sideways. There is no way that I'm going to forfeit even a nickel—I've got plans for that money!

Newspapers in 1953 have smaller type, more columns and so more stories on their front pages. On this Monday the two main headlines read, *Ship Sabotage Clues Hunted* and *Rain Record Set*. Heck! I know that just from being out in it.

I fold forty-seven papers and carry five flat. Monday editions are average size, but even fifty-two average-size copies of the *Oregon Journal* weigh a lot more than I bargain for. How am I going to lug them all the way out to my bike? The bigger boys and J. P. are watching me, but no one offers to help. Apparently this is some kind of test. Finally I ease one of the bags off the counter, duck down and stick my head through the opening between them, then straighten up wearing the bags like a poncho.

With as much dignity as I can muster, I walk out through Benny's, duck again, slip the bags over the carrier stand and tie them in place.

Mission accomplished!

Archer's route is over behind Crawford School on the eastern edge of town. It's a mixture of older and newer houses, and for the first forty deliveries, everything goes smoothly. I lob the triangle-folded papers carefully onto porches, put three of the five flats in tubes under mailboxes, place one behind a screen dor as instructed on the list and shove another through a mail slot. At first I carefully check off each house as soon as I leave the paper. Then I get two houses before checking off. Then three. With a dozen or so houses left, I start getting fancy. That's my undoing.

I'm already throwing overhand from farther out. The porches along Logan street are large and my aim is good, so I hit eight in a row from 25-30 feet. The fortieth paper lands on a doormat just six inches from a dozing cat and scares the bejeezus out of it. I laugh and reach for the forty-first.

This time it's a small open porch on the far front corner of the house. My first thought is to stop and lob or walk it up, but it's only twenty-five feet from the curb and I have a streak going. So I zip up a driveway onto the sidewalk to cut the distance a bit more, set my index finger along the crease of the triangle, cock my arm like a gun and let fly as I roll past.

Very bad idea!

I forget to allow for the fact that I'm moving past the target as I throw, so the paper sails wide to the left and lands in a puddle by the driveway—a small puddle, the only one on the lawn, one that I could never hit if I aim for it. But here I am with twelve more deliveries to make and eleven more papers left in the bags.

Automatically, I deliver them, carefully checking each house off and making sure I don't ruin another paper. But what am I going to do for Archer's place? Maybe J. P. is still back at Benny's and can give me an extra. It may cost me a nickel, but I lose that anyway if the Archers complain. So I ride back to Third Street as fast as I can, but J. P.'s old Chevy is gone.

I find Benny back in his workshop, assembling another bike. "Do you know where J. P. is?" I ask hopefully.

"Left twenty minutes ago. He's probably gone home. What's the problem?"I hold up the soggy paper and say,

"I missed."

"Oh, don't worry about that. He always leaves four or five extras in the box under the counter. The one Jill uses."

I run back to the *Journal* room, dump off the ruined paper, pick up a clean one and race back out. After a two-second wrestling match with my conscience, I say to Benny, "Tell J. P. I took an extra. If he wants to charge me for it, it's okay."

"Don't worry," Benny says without looking up. "They're for emergencies just like that one. He never charges for them."

I don't have a watch yet, but I know it's getting close to five by the time I find Archer's house. I'm not sure if the sun is down, because I haven't seen it all day, but the light is definitely starting to fade. I'm sure I'm late, but maybe if I hand the paper to them and apologize, they won't get mad and complain. So I walk up and knock on the front door. When a woman opens it, I hand over the paper and say, "I'm Alec Lewis. I'm filling in for Dave while he's sick. Sorry if I'm a bit late with your paper."

The lady smiles and says, "Oh, you're not late at all. It's so nice of you to help David this way. But you didn't have to come up and hand it to me."

"Well, I just wanted to know how Dave is doing and, uh, maybe say hi to him."

"Oh, I'm so glad you're concerned," she replies, "but I'm afraid you can't see him now. He's been flat on his back all day, poor boy. I'm afraid he'll be out for the rest of the week."

I try to hide a smile as I tell her, "Well, I hope he feels better soon."

Yeah, just not *too* soon.

On Monday nights I always listen to *The Lone Ranger* on KEX and then *The Cisco Kid* on KPOJ. Mary Alice gets to watch *Hopalong Cassidy* on KPTV. Lucky dog! I always read the comic strip in the *Journal*, but I never get a chance to watch the program. Hey, maybe if she's my girlfriend, I could sometime…

On Tuesday J. P. greets me with a stony face and says, "I got one call last night, Alec."

My heart seems to do a skip and a thump, like a bad dancer missing a step. Who? Where? I'm sure I didn't miss anyone. Did someone see me almost clobber that cat?

Then he smiles as he takes out the Prince Albert and starts filling his pipe. "It wasn't a complaint. It was a compliment.

Dave's mother called to say you're a real young gentleman." He looks around the room as he digs out the kitchen match and adds, as he strikes it, "Now *that's* a first for this outfit!"

"I did ruin a paper," I admit. "Missed the porch and threw it right in the mud."

"That's why we have extras," J. P. says as he lights up. "You might want to start carrying one or two." He hands me two quarters and then says, "C'mon. I'll buy you a pepsi."

Suddenly I feel like a man among men. J. P. Harrington doesn't buy you a pepsi unless you do something really special, like bring in a new subscription. Wait till Dad hears about this!

****

The journal I promise to do for Aunt Emma is starting to take shape. I save articles about Eisenhower's inauguration and the ongoing war in Korea. (Eisenhower promises, "Peace with honor.") I also save some of the local and statewide news. Five days after Washington hangs the Wilson brothers, Oregon puts two men to death in its gas chamber. Morris Leland dies for murdering a 15-year-old girl, and Franklin Payne for killing a grocer during a holdup. Both men confess their guilt.

Odd, quirky things also catch my eye. On January 7 the *Journal* reports a man driving into a used car lot, leaving his own car and hobbling over to a newer one on crutches and asking to take it for a test drive. He promises to return in two hours, but he never comes back. When the salesmen check his old car, they find he has left his wooden leg and a trunk full of still-wrapped Christmas presents.

On the 5th I find a story about an army corporal who goes AWOL from his unit at Fort Knox, Kentucky, and then gets himself shipped out for Korea. He makes his way clear to the front, where he poses as a replacement and joins up and fights with the 72nd tank battalion for several months before finally confessing his true identity. He is fined ten dollars, but permitted to remain with his new unit.

On January 10 a guy named Bevo Francis, playing basketball for Rio Grande college in Ohio, scores 116 points in a single game. (His team wins, 150-85.)

And on the 9th a Negro woman named Frankie Baker dies ("senile and insane," the *Journal* reports) in a mental hospital over in Pendleton. But back in St, Louis in 1899, she shoots and kills her boyfriend, Albert Britt, because, "He done her wrong." The incident becomes a song, *Frankie and Albert,* which is later changed to *Frankie and Johnnie.* Frankie apparently gets away with it, but she never gets to cash in on her fame, and eventually it drives her crazy.

Dad's only comment when I show him the story is, "Wow! To think someone like her winds up dying in Pendleton, Oregon!" I decide to call these stories "quirkies" and save a special place in my journal for them.

But as I collect and save these stories, something very obvious but very important occurs to me. *Somebody writes them!* There are people who make their living going to faraway places, meeting important people, investigating strange happenings and writing about them. They actually get paid to do it!

I know Dad's job is important, but it's hardly glamorous. All he really does is check people's math for them. The store clerks don't do much more than stand behind counters and fetch things all day. O'Dell's mechanics spend their time taking cars apart and putting them back together again. But imagine going to Korea to report on the war or back east to see President Eisenhower inagurated—heck, all the way to England to see Queen Elizabeth crowned! Some people get to do it Maybe, someday, could I be one of them?

****

Dirty Dave is out for one full, glorious, soggy week. By Friday everyone treats me like one of the crew. Well, everybody but Jill, but she doesn't really count. When I casually say, "Hi, Twerp," she bristles like a cat confronted by a strange dog.

"Beat him up, Kenny!" she pleads. "He called me a bad name!"

"He's one of us now, Twerp. Get used to it."

"Double uck!" she growls, and stomps back to the front.

On Saturday J.P. gives me a fifty-cent piece, puts one bulldog in with my regular Saturdays and tells me Dave will probably be back on Monday. "Do you think you can do the Sunday route by yourself?" he asks. "I can get you help if you need it, but there's a bonus if you can do it solo with no complaints."

"How much?"

"An extra quarter, plus I'll buy you coffee at the hotel."

Oooh man! That would make $3.75 for the week. Add in my allowance, and I could have $4.25 in my pocket by Monday. Enough for something very special. Something I have drooled over for weeks now.

"Sure," I tell J. P. "I can do it by myself. Just give me the Sunday route list."

****

Yet another wet, cold Sunday morning, my fifth, but this time I'm working alone. I'm not just a helper now. This morning it's for real.

The toughest part is getting out of bed when the alarm goes off. I get dressed quickly and grab a cookie to munch on as I jam a stocking cap on my head and struggle into my heavy winter jacket. Mom has stuffed a flashlight and another cookie into the pockets. Then I bump my bike down the front steps, hop aboard and ride off into the lonely darkness.

J. P. is waiting down at the Flying-A station. Pietrowski, Rush and Reed are loading papers, but taking their time about it. Another carrier, Doug Dixon, comes in a few seconds after me. I know his route goes clear out to the south edge of town, past the college, but I've never ridden with him.

J. P. points to my stack of fifty-three papers and says, "Take thirty, then come back and get the rest. They're bigger than usual this morning." Among the things I've noticed about J. P. is that he never raises his voice, but he has two distinct tones. One is the suggestion tone, and the other is a direct order. You don't argue with that one, so I load fifteen in each bag and head up Third Street past Benny's and across the tracks.

Once again I feel the absence of all the little sounds of life. The rain is a cold drizzle that settles on my coat and cap as silently as snowflakes. Cars along the curbs or in driveways seem like huge hibernating bears. I must be the only living, moving being for blocks, so I start whistling softly, just to break the silence. *S-i-g-n-a-l, Signal!* Then I hear the purr of an engine. Headlights jab around a corner, catch me in their beams and hold me there as the car glides to a stop. I freeze in a panic for a second, then notice the lights on the top and relax.

Officer Derflinger (Old Dirty Fingers, we call him behind his back) rolls down his window and asks, "Are you the new kid?"

"Yessir. Alec Lewis. Archer has the flu."

"Okay. J. P. asked me to watch out for you. You doin' all right?"

"Sure," I say. Maybe it's the dawn coming or maybe it's just knowing Officer Dirty Fingers is around, but the night suddenly seems a bit lighter and less threatening. Still, I feel duty bound to act just a little annoyed. "I'm fine," I add, trying to put a little gruffness that I don't really feel in my voice.

"That's good. Everything's quiet. Kyle Everson's a couple blocks up and three over. He has the *Oregonian* route out here. Nice guy." He rolls the window back up and drives away, and I'm left with the rain and the silence again.

I deliver the first thirty papers, then race back to the Flying-A station to get the rest. This is going to be a lot easier than I thought. J. P. is still at the station when I pull in.

"Any problems?" he asks.

"Nope," I answer as I restuff the bags.

"Did you see the patrol officer?"

"Old Officer Dirty Fingers? Yeah. We talked for a few minutes." I catch J. P.'s frown and quickly add, "Don't worry. I didn't call him that. I'd never say that to his face."

J. P. takes a long pull at his pipe and blows a cloud of smoke my way. "Then why say it behind his back?" he asks. "There's a saying I learned back when I was a kid. It goes:

'Words unexpressed can sometimes fall back dead,
But God Himself can't kill them once they're said!'

Do you know what that means?"

"Uh, yes. I think so."

"It means that words have a way of getting back to the people they're spoken about. Do you want Officer Derflinger for a friend or an enemy?"

That doesn't take much thought. "A friend."

"Then don't make fun of his name. Don't make fun of anyone's name or background. He could be a subscriber or a good friend of one." He removes the pipe and points the stem at me like a gun again. "A snotty kid can cost me a dozen subscribers just by shooting off his mouth. I've had it happen once or twice. Those kids don't work for me anymore. Remember that!"

As I do the second part of the route and then head back past the station to get Archer's place, I ponder J. P.'s words. Maybe it is unfair to call him Officer Dirty Fingers, even though he's practically asking for it with a name like Derflinger. I mean, that's different from the team calling me Butterfinger or the girls calling Mary Alice Miss Peepants, since I did drop the ball and she did wet herself.

Or is it?'

There are words that we as kids are not supposed to say, and names that we as kids are not supposed to use. We know that, and yet we hear the grownups say and use them all the time. Mom and Dad watch their language pretty closely, at least around me. But not everybody does, and I've picked up a whole litany of offensive terms that I'm not supposed to know—words like *jigaboo, spic, nigger, gook, wop, kike, polack, bohunk, wetback, joad, greaser, redskin, jap*—and I'm sure there's lots more. Well, where do you suppose we first hear them? Racial and ethnic tolerance are pretty well unknown in 1953.

But how does it feel to be on the receiving end? I know Archer doesn't mind being called Dirty Dave. He practically glories in it. Jill lets Scott and the others call her Twerp, but she bristles when I do it. Then there's poor Mary Alice, branded because of an accident four years ago. It must really hurt when you can't hit back.

I'm still thinking about this when I meet J. P. for coffee at the Oregon Hotel. He seems to sense my thoughts, for he suddenly breaks the silence.

"Names can really hurt, can't they?"

"Yeah," I answer, then suddenly look up at him. "How did you know—?"

"It's all over your face. You've been thinking about what you called Derflinger. I'll bet you won't do it again. Just like that porch you missed Monday—have you missed it since?"

"Nosir. Six for six," I answer.

"That's good. See, I don't mind you screwing up or making a mistake. That's a part of learning. I only get mad when you repeat the screwups." He pauses for a sip. "I got good and mad at Archer a couple of times. Nearly fired him, in fact."

"Because of his jokes?" I ask. "You know we call him—"

"Dirty Dave," he finishes it for me. "Yes, I know all about that. He had to learn when to open his mouth and when to keep it shut. It took him a while, but he finally figured it out. He knows now that the jokes are okay if he's in the back room, keeps his voice down and Jill isn't around. And he knows now that as soon as he leaves the room with his papers, he's a representative of the *Oregon Journal*, and he behaves himself accordingly."

He takes another sip and then says, "You're going to learn a lot faster than he did. In fact, I'll wager you've got it down already."

J. P. takes a dollar from his billfold and hands it over. "Here's the fifty cents, plus a quarter for doing the Sunday route solo and another if you'll promise always to be careful about what you say and treat everyone on your route just a little better than they might deserve. Think you can do that?

"I'll sure try, Sir," I say as I pocket the dollar.

J. P. pats me on the shoulder. "I think you're going to be a good one," he says. "Maybe one of the best."

Chapter Six: The Idea

Archer returns on Monday, February 2, and I have to go back to being a tagalong once more. Maybe someone else will get sick, but all the *Journal* carriers look pretty healthy when I check in with J. P. after school. April, when I get to take over Madigan's route, seems a long way off.

But hey, I have four dollars, plus my allowance, and they're burning a hole in my pocket. So I stop off at the hardware store just a block from Benny's to pick out a new knife I've been wanting since Christmas. Dad has set out the rules. I can have a new knife, but I have to pay for it myself, and no switchblades—even though they're still legal in 1953.

So it will have to be a clasp knife, but Old Man Taylor has some beauts in his display case. I show my money to the clerk, and he takes three or four out and lets me hold them. I finally pick out one with red and gold stripes on a handle with just a suggestion of curve to it. The blade measures three and seven-eighths inches. That's just what I want, since I can't carry it to school unless the blade is under four inches long.

Take a knife to school? Sure, ever since third grade, when we join cub scouts. The jackknife is considered part of the uniform. (Well, *we* consider it part of the uniform.) From there it's an easy step to any kind of pocket knife. By fifth grade most boys and quite a few girls carry them every day.

In February's rain, while we're cooped up in the gym, they have to stay in our pockets. But when spring comes, if it ever comes, and we get to go outside for recess and at noon, then they'll come out. We've developed a game we call mumblestretch—a combination of mumbletypeg and stretch—and we'll have nine or ten games going at once all over the playground. Mr. Hunter and Mr. Jackson keep a sharp watch to make sure we aren't playing chicken, which is like stretch in reverse, but stretch, mumblestretch and mumbletypeg are okay.

Boys play against boys and girls against girls. That's part of our unwritten code. Janet Tabor, who is still the tallest kid in the class and can do the full splits besides, would like to challenge some of us. But no boy, including me, wants to get beat by a girl, so we always refuse unless she's wearing a tight skirt. Then she can't play and gets very mad, which is fine with us.

Yet none of us would dream of threatening someone with a knife or using one in a fight. Yes, there are occasional fights, especially between sixth-grade boys after Christmas break. One day I overhear Mr. Hunter complaining to Mrs. Foster, "Good Lord! The boys are starting to notice the girls already! I swear it happens earlier every year."

"It must be all these new vitamins," Mrs. Foster says. "You'd better get the gloves out."

It's a spring ritual at Cozine, and in 1953 I guess it starts early. The sixth-grade boys strut and preen themselves like peacocks, while the girls gather in bunches and giggle at them. We fifth-graders look on and think, *Cripes! Am I going to get goofy like that next year?*

The strutting and preening of course leads to squabbles. Mr. Hunter or Mr. Jackson pull the two showoffs apart and ask them if they really want to fight. If both answer yes and look evenly matched, they're told they'll get their chance in the gym next recess. When the rest of us troop in, we see the mats down at the boys' end and Mr. Hunter or Mr. Jackson tying the gloves on the two fighters.

As we form an excited ring around the mats and the girls come across the line to join us, Mr. Hunter shoves a tooth protector into each fighter's mouth, while Mr. Jackson pulls out a stopwatch. The two fighters touch gloves, then Mr. Jackson tells them, "Go to it!"

I realize later that the gloves are so big and heavily padded that the bout is little more than a glorified pillow fight. There is never any real boxing either. The two fighters just stand toe to toe and flail away at each other until one gets staggered or they're both so tired they can barely hold their arms up. Then Mr. Jackson calls time, declares the bout a draw and makes the two fighters shake hands. This happens about once a week in the winter and spring of 1953.

The girls, expecially the sixth-graders, make a big show of being horrified and disgusted, but I notice almost all of them come over the line to watch. Personally, I think fighting over a girl is pretty stupid. But one afternoon in February, while two sixth-grade boys are going at it, I look around and notice Mary Alice down at the far end of the gym practically by herself. So I back away from the crowd, pick up a basketball, go over to one of the side baskets on the line and start shooting layups.

The line is the half-court stripe on the basketball court, and it divides the gym in half. Boys stay on the north side, girls on the south. I don't know if there's a written rule, but it's always been that way. If we boys want to play basketball at recess, we go side to side across the court, using either the pair of baskets at the north end or those at the half-court line. The pair at the south end go unused. Girls do not play basketball in 1953.

I hit a few easy ones, then deliberately miss with a hard driving shot that caroms off the backboard and down to the south end. I take a couple steps over the line and wait for some girl to retrieve it and throw it back. I'm hoping it's

Mary Alice. Sure enough, she chases it down, walks a few paces toward me and lobs it back. I give her a smile and a wave, then drive and shoot again. All the while the two pillow fighters are pounding away at each other.

I catch the ball as it drops through the net, spin and, sure enough, she's still watching me. Okay, good. I dribble a few steps toward her, stop and ask, "Want to take a shot?"

She blushes and shakes her head, but she doesn't retreat.

"Aw, c'mon," I urge, holding out the ball. "I bet you could make one."

She hesitates, and for a second it looks like she'll take me up on it. Then Mr. Jackson blows his whistle, ending the fight, and the girls troop back to their end of the gym. Mary Alice runs to join them, and I'm left holding a basketball and wondering about what might have been.

"Boys!" I hear one sixth-grade girl say to another as they cross back over the line, "Why do they do dumb things like that?"

"Because we know you like to watch us do them," I answer her.

She stops, turns and looks me up and down like I was something unpleasant she had just stepped in. "Who asked *you*, Squirt?" she snarls, then turns and walks away.

Girls! How do you ever figure them out?

****

I decide I need some expert help with this, but where can I get it? Dad gets nervous if I even mention Mary Alice's name. Mom always goes along with Dad. I don't have any older brothers, not even—Aha!

Ken Scott, master trickster and general know-it-all. I haven't ridden with him for more than three weeks, but I bet he could fill me in on just about anything.

I approach him on Monday the 16th, the day the main headline reads *Atom Spies Execution Date Reset*, and ask if I can ride along.

"Sure," he says, "if you'll fold the papers while I go get a pepsi."

So I'm back to folding papers for free. Scott offers me a swig from the pepsi and I take it, hoping he hasn't spit in it first. We pass Jill on the way out and I say, "Hello—Jill," with just enough of a pause that she knows what I'm thinking. Some girls are just meant to be teased.

"Ken," I say after we've delivered three or four houses. "Can I ask you something?"

"Sure. What?" he replies.

"Do you have a girlfriend?"

"Yeah. Why do you wanta know that?"

"How did you do it? I mean, how did you get her? That is, what made her your girlfriend?"

"I asked her." He pauses to throw another paper, then says, "How come you're so interested in my love life all of a sudden?"

"Well, there's this girl in my class, and I—that is, I'd like her to be—you know."

"Ho ho!" he chuckles. "You got the hots for some chick and you need a little advice from the old pro. *That's* why you wanted to come with me today, huh?"

"Well, I thought..."

"Relax, Kid. Old Uncle Kenny can fill you in. What's the matter? She doesn't like you?"

"No. She does."

"You sure?" he asks.

"Pretty sure. I kissed her once."

"Did she slug you for doin' it?"

"No, she kissed me back."

"Shoot!" Ken exclaims as he throws another paper. "You're around first base already. So what's the big problem?"

"I can't be around her. Not at school. Everyone will laugh at us."

"Go over to her house then." Ken suggests.

"Can't. Her mom caught us once and now she watches all the time. And she has two big brothers who'd probably pound on me."

"Ask her over to your house then."

"She can't come, and I can't see her after school because she has to go right home and I have to come down to Benny's."

"All right, you have a problem," Scott admits. "Let me think for a while."

We work another ten minutes in silence before Scott says,"I think I've got an idea.The library's onMadigan's route,right?"

"Yeah. We take the daily in and put the Sunday through the book return slot."

"Okay, here's what you can do. They have a junior volunteer program for kids after school and during the summer, so they can learn about how libraries work. My sister tried it once. Said it was kinda boring. But get this girl to sign up for it. Maybe just once or twice a week, so her mom doesn't get suspicious. Then you can meet her there when you bring the paper."

"Or on my way home after I finish," I add with a grin. "Wow! Why didn't I think of that?"

"Because you're still wet behind the ears, Kid. Four or five years of experience and you'll be as smooth as Old Kenny. And you'll get that delivering the *Journal*. Yeah, I could tell you about some times..."

Scott's voice trails off and his face takes on that I-know-something-that-you-don't smirk that bigger guys like to use around kids my age. That makes me mad. I'm going to be one of the gang pretty soon, so I figure it's time I'm let in on the secrets.

"All right, tell me about some," I say.

Scott looks around to make sure we're alone, then drops his voice to a confidential mutter. "Okay, it was just over a year ago, in January, when I had to do Carl Ferris' route for a few days. He got hit with appendicitis on a Saturday night, and they had to rush him to the hospital and take it out. J. P. calls me that night and asks me to do his route too Sunday morning, since I'm the next oldest guy."

"Who's Ferris?" I ask.

"He had the route Pat Rush has now. He quit when he turned sixteen last June. Anyhow, I have to get up an hour earlier, run through my route like a dose of salts through the hired hand, then grab a list from J. P. and start in on Carl's. I'm setting those papers out as fast as I can and trying to get finished before the sun comes up, 'cause that's when the early birds start to complain.

"One of the last places is the Evans house. The instructions say to open the garage door and leave it by the door going into the house. Now remember, it's January and colder than a wart on a welldigger's butt. I got on a heavy coat and a stocking cap pulled down over my forehead clear to the eyebrows. I'm in a two-car garage, but there's just one car in it.

"Well, I'm standing there with the paper, trying to spot the dang step, when a light comes on, and there's Patsy Evans standing there in a bathrobe and slippers. Before I can say anything, she says, 'It's about time, Carl! I've been freezing my buns off!' Then she drops the robe and she's standing there naked as a jaybird!"

"Except for the slippers," I say.

"Kid, I wasn't looking at her feet!"

"What did you do?" I ask.

"I was so dang shocked I didn't do anything—I just stood there staring. I remember she put her hands on her hips and said, 'Well, c'mon! It's not like you haven't seen it all before. Shut the door before somebody drives by.' See, it's dark where I was standing, and I had a dark coat like Carl and was about the same size. It wasn't till I pulled the garage door back down and took a step toward her that she realized it wasn't Carl."

"What did she do then?" I ask.

"She looked more mad than scared. She just says, 'What are *you* doin' here? You're not Carl!' I blurt out something about Carl being rushed to the hospital and me having to take his place. She just says 'Oh,' and picks up her robe and puts it back on. Then she says, 'Well, give me the paper,' just as cool as can be. I gotta give her credit for that."

"Then what happened?"

"Nothing. She takes the paper and walks back into the house. Never asks about Carl. He could be lying stone-cold dead for all she seems to care. She just looks back over her shoulder, gives me a little smile and says, 'You don't say anything, and I won't say anything. Okay?"

So maybe Scott's story is true and maybe it's pure b.s., but just hearing it somehow makes me feel accepted. I know that Patsy is the big sister of Sandy Evans, the girl I study comparative anatomy with back in kindergarten until we get caught at it. Maybe it runs in the family.

Now, if only Dirty Dave would tell me a joke, I'd really feel like one of the group.

****

Tuesday morning and it's raining again, but not hard enough for Mom to drive me to school. I know that Mary Alice's mother will take her, though, so there will be no chance to talk to her by the bike stand. I give her a smile and a wave when we meet in the hall on the way to class. She blushes a little and smiles back.

The *Journal* headlines that afternoon announce that President Eisenhower is certain the Russians have exploded a hydrogen bomb. I tag along with Madigan, and we zip through his route in near-record time. After we finish I head back to the library and ask the lady at the main desk about their junior volunteer program.

Yes, she tells me, they still do have the program, though not many children seem interested in it these days. Yes, someone my age would be eligible, though they would prefer someone a year or two older. But no, they've never had a boy volunteer before. Would I be interested?

"No," I say. "I'll be delivering the paper here. But I have a friend and she might be interested." The librarian's eyebrows arch slightly.

"Well, have her come in and talk to me," she says.

Thank you, Ken Scott! You can con me into folding your papers any day!

Wednesday it's overcast, but the rain holds off. I leave for school a few minutes early and cut over to Yamhill Street to see if I can spot Mary Alice coming down The Hill. Yep, there she is, taking it slow and stopping at almost every corner. I think back to November when I come roaring down and wind up nearly splattering Pat Rush and myself all over the street. It seems like a long time ago now.

Mary Alice looks a bit surprised, but not upset or angry. "What are you doing over here?" she asks.

"Looking for you," I tell her.

"Why?"

"I want to see you." A car comes down The Hill and we move over to the sidewalk. "Can I talk with you for a minute?" I know I sound bolder than I feel. Someone who knows both of us could come by at any moment. Mary Alice must sense this too, for she looks around nervously.

"What do you want to see me about?"

Now I'm the one who's confused. "I—I just want to see you." I know I'm scrambling for words, but this is new territory for me.

"Alec, we're in the same room. You see me every day." She still looks puzzled, but makes no effort to leave.

"Yeah, but—well—I have something I want to give you."

"What? Here?" Now she's confused again. This is getting us nowhere fast.

"Look," I say. "It's kinda hard to explain right here. Could I ride back with you tonight after school?"

"I can't have you up to the house. Mom says only girls for company. No boys."

"Okay, I'll just come part way. That would be all right, wouldn't it?"

"Yeah. I guess it would," she agrees.

"Of course, if you don't want me to—"

"No. It's okay," she says, and we ride down The Hill and leave it at that.

I'm not much of a student for the rest of the day, since I'm trying desperately to figure out just how to tell her everything that's on my mind. I come up with half a dozen little speeches, but they all seem corny and, even worse, phony. Finally I decide just to let it come out and hope it makes sense. We both take our time leaving at the end of the day, and most of the bikes are gone by the time we pull ours out.

I follow her up Yamhill Street to the base of The Hill. She gears down and starts the climb. One block. Two blocks. Suddenly I'm afraid she's just going to keep going all the way home and leave me hung out to dry, but she finally stops and the end of the second block.

"All right, Alec. What is it you want?" she asks.

"I have something I want to give you," I tell her. "But I don't want to bring it to school, and I can't take it up to your house."

"What is it?"

"I want it to be a surprise, but it's something you'd like."

She gives me a funny look and asks, "Why do you want to give me something?"

"Because I like you. I really do!" There, it's out!

She blushes and answers very softly, "I like you too, Alec."

"Well, that's why I want to see you. Do you want to see me?"

"Yes, but Mom says no boys up at the house."

"Then here's what you can do." I quickly repeat what I've learned about the junior volunteer program at the library, leaving out the fact that I got the idea from Ken Scott. She listens, then smiles, then nods.

"It might work," she says. "I'll ask Mom about it, but I've got to get going now."

She pedals away as I turn the old Columbia around, stick my feet up on the bars and go ripping down The Hill just like I do in November.

****

"It worked, huh?" Scott asks as I help him fold papers. I'm riding with Madigan, but I figure I owe Scott something for his scheme.

"Well, she likes the idea, and she's gonna ask about it."

"Hey, man! You're in like Flynn!" he says as we finish up. "Mind if I give you a couple pieces of advice?"

"Sure," I say as we haul the papers out to his bike. It's Wednesday and the headlines announce out jets have shot down seven MIGs in the skies over Korea.

First, stop in at the library today, and go at least one day a week when she's not gonna be there. That way they'll think you're interested in the books and not just in her."

"Okay, that makes sense."

"Second, get to know the librarian. Find out her name and make sure she knows yours."

"Why should I do that?"

"They always cut you more slack when they know who you are. She's a librarian, so ask her something about books."

Ken tosses this off casually, but, because I take it, my life changes once again. I stop off on my way home from the route, formally introduce myself to the lady at the front desk, and try to think of a question that doesn't sound totally stupid.

"Uh, could you help me find a book?" Not very original, but the best I can come up with.

"Ah!" she says, smiling. "You're the young man who's going to be delivering the paper. What kind of book are you interested in? We have several thousand here." She's gray and wrinkled and smells faintly of lavender, which I guess is how a librarian is supposed to be. But her name is Mrs. Carruthers, not Miss.

"Newspapers!" I say with a sudden flash of inspiration. "Someday I'd like to write for one. Maybe be an editor. Is there anything…?"

She looks me over carefully, as if I'm a new volume she doesn't know quite where to shelve. "How old are you?" she asks. "Are you a good reader?"

"I'm eleven, but I can read real good. I always score high on the tests."

"Well then, you might try this."

She walks over to a shelf, pulls down a volume and hands it to me. I read the title, *Here Is Your War*. The author's name is Ernie Pyle. It's over 300 pages and the print is kinda small.

"What's it about?" I ask.

"Pyle was a war correspondent," she says. "This book is about his experiences covering the war in North Africa. It's not a children's book," she warns, "but if you're a good reader, you should be able to get through it. If you do, this is the sequel. It's even longer."

I peer at the title, *Brave Men*. Another book about World War II. What am I getting myself into here? Mrs. Carruthers seems to sense my uncertainty.

"Yes. They're long books. You don't read them all at one sitting. Do ten pages a night and you'll finish the first in about a month."

"A whole month on one book?"

"Then do twenty and finish in half the time. A good book is worth every minute you spend on it. A bad one isn't worth two seconds. But of course, if you don't think you're a good enough reader…"

Of course that locks me into reading it. The surest way to get me to bust my tail on something is to suggest that I might not be good enough to do it.

So I walk out of the library with a book by Ernie Pyle tucked under my arm, a book that will influence me as much as any I will ever read. Thanks again, Ken.

Mrs. Carruthers doesn't ask about my friend, and for that I'm grateful.

Chapter Seven: The Game

On March 4th the *Journal*'s main headline reads, *No News About Stalin; Is He Dead?* My classmates and I sure hope he is. We are just too young to remember when Hitler is alive, so Old Joe Stalin is the arch-bogeyman our parents threaten us with when they want us to shape up.

On the 5th the headline says, *Stalin's Heart Fails, End Near.* The next day his death is confirmed in the papers, and somebody named Georgi Malenkov takes over as headman of the Soviet Union. Mom and Dad rejoice because Stalin's death might mean an end to the war in Korea. My classmates and I are just happy that another bogeyman is dead. Someone makes up a verse about it, and on a rare sunny day in March, groups of us link arms and march around the playground chanting,

Stalin's dead! So we said,
"Hurrah! Hooray! That's one less Red!"

"Funny, isn't it?" Dad comments when I recite the verse for him that night. "Ten years ago he was our great ally, and we sacrificed ships and men to send supplies to him through Murmansk. Twenty years ago your Aunt Emma thought Stalin would be the savior of the world. Nowadays, anyone who thought that way is likely to get hauled up before the Un-American Activities Committee."

"Does that mean that Aunt Emma is going to get in trouble?" I ask. I've read a little about Senator Joe McCarthy, who seems to be hunting for communists just about everywhere. I've heard some people say he's a patriot and others say he's a fool. Some folks call him a great man and others call him a dangerous witch-hunter.

Dad just shakes his head and refuses to get into a discussion about it. "Your Aunt Emma can take care of herself," he says. "I wouldn't worry too much about her."

****

Here Is Your War is slow reading, but after two or three days I get caught up in it and make steady progress. I'm not going to get through it in two weeks, though. So on Friday the 6th, after helping Madigan, I take the book back to renew it. As Mrs. Carruthers restamps the due date, she says, "Your friend started working here today. Would you like to say hello to her?"

She points to the children's section, where I see Mary Alice shelving books. She smiles and blushes again when she sees me. "Okay," she says. "I'm here. When are you going to get me that present?"

"As soon as I can get home and get back with it," I tell her.

I'm back in five minutes with the Niewport. Of course my carefully thought-out little presentation speech goes flying out of my head, so I wind up saying, "Here. I thought you would like to have this."

Mary Alice looks at the plane, then at me, and her eyes start to tear up again. She wants to say something, but we're both aware of Mrs. Carruthers watching us. So she takes it over to show the librarian and tells her briefly about her Uncle Quentin.

"Very good workmanship," Mrs. Carruthers comments. "Mary Alice, why don't you put it in the back room where it will be safe? Alec can go with you, if he would like. But mind you, just for a minute!"

In the back room Mary Alice carefully sets the model on a shelf. Then she gives me a hug and kisses me on the cheek. She has to stand on tiptoe to do it. "Thank you! It's beautiful." She whispers this, even though we're alone.

I see her big sad eyes tearing up again so, without thinking, I pull out a none-too-clean handkerchief that Mom makes me carry in the winter and try to wipe them dry. *Oh Jeez!* I realize. *I blew my nose in it this afternoon!* For one awful instant I can picture the headline: *Boy Blinds Girl With Snot!* But apparently Mary Alice is unharmed.

"I hoped you'd like it," I say. "I don't know what personal insignia your uncle had, so I painted his initials by the cockpit."

"I'd better keep it here for now," she says. "I don't know if Mom's going to like the idea of you giving me a present, especially one you made."

"What about your dad?"

"It's funny. I thought Dad would object to me working here and Mom would stick up for me, but it was the other way round. Mom didn't like it at first and Dad talked her into it."

"That's good, isn't it?"

"I don't know, Alec. When he acts like that, it means he's up to something. He's changed his mind about Ron's girlfriend too. It's like he's trying to be buddies with us all of a sudden. He's got some kind of plan. I don't know what it is, but it scares me a little."

"Hey! At least you're here and we can see each other. How often do you come in?"

"Mondays and Fridays till 5:30. Mom drops me off and Ron picks me up on his way home from practice. He has a car now. They may let me come Wednesdays too, if I like it and do a good job."

I sure hope you do then," I tell her. I get another hug and a quick kiss, and we go back out to face the world and Mrs. Carruthers.

****

I figure Dad will be the one to help me get through *Here Is Your War*, but instead it's Mom who gets all enthusiastic. "Ernie Pyle!" she says. "A great newspaperman! I remember reading his columns even before the war. And of course his war reporting was superb, as I hope you are finding out."

"Yeah, he's good, but kinda hard to read sometimes. What happened to him?"

"He was killed during the last months of the war in the Pacific. A Japanese sniper shot him." She pauses for a grim smile. "It can be a dangerous job sometimes. Did I ever tell you I was going to be a reporter once?"

That's news to me. Mom and Dad never talk much about their pasts. I know Mom went to the University of Oregon for a couple of years before she met and married Dad, and I know Dad never served during the war. Maybe that's why he doesn't like to read about it. I know it's a touchy subject, but I decide to ask Mom anyway.

"Why wasn't Dad in the war. I know he wasn't too old."

"He wanted to enlist right after Pearl Harbor, even though he was married and you were about ready to arrive. But he couldn't pass the physical."

"What was wrong?" I know Dad's no athlete, but he looks healthy enough.

Mom is silent for a little while, apparently debating with herself. "Don't ever let him know I told you this, Alec. Flat feet! They might still have taken him if he was single, but not when he was married and about to become a father."

For a minute I'm sorry Dad isn't a war hero. Then I think, *suppose they do take him and he becomes a hero, but gets himself killed doing it*? Where would Mom and I be then? It's great to have a hero in the family, I guess, but a live dad beats a dead hero any day.

I have almost as much trouble picturing Mom as Brenda Starr, Girl Reporter. (That's a comic strip that runs in *The*

Oregonian.) The girls in my class, with the possible exception of Janet, don't seem to want to be anything more than teachers, nurses or secretaries. That's until they can get married—though not to drips like us, they make it known—and start raising children of their own.

"Alec, you can't see me as I was fifteen or twenty years ago, before the war, in the middle of the depression," Mom says. "It was a different world then, a tougher world. All we had were dreams, so we dreamed big—girls as well as boys. I was going to fly like Amelia Earhart or become a glamorous actress like Jean Harlow. Of course I knew, deep in my heart, that it would never happen. But then I thought, all right. I can do the next best thing."

"What was that?"

"I could become a reporter and meet these people and learn about them and what made them great. So I did, in high school and through two years of college. I met lots of people, some good and some bad, nobody really famous, but a few who were almost famous. But there was only one I really considered great—and I wound up marrying him."

"You gave up your job to marry Dad?"

"And aren't you glad I did?" She says it with a smile, but I can hear a wistful tone in her voice. "It's called sacrifice, just like the batter who gives himself up to advance the runner. It may not be glamorous, but sometimes it's worth it." She smiles again and ruffles my hair. "In your case, it was worth it."

She says no more, but her last sentence leaves me a little choked up, and I start to develop a new respect for girls in general and Mom in particular. *Sacrifice.* I hear the word used often, in and out of baseball, but until now I never appreciate the terrible power behind its meaning.

I will learn a lot more about it before the year is over.

****

It's Wednesday, March 11, about 6:45 p.m. We finish dinner early. Dad and I help Mom get the dishes done, and now

Dad's reading the sports page, while I'm cutting out another quirkie for my journal as we listen to *What's My Line?* on KEX.. This quirkie is about "Fainting Fanny"—a woman who pulls a fainting act on busses up in Portland and then collects money from sympathetic riders when she tells them she faints because he hasn't eaten for two or three days. But she makes the mistake of trying it a second time on the same bus. The driver remembers her, calls the police, and Fainting Fanny is jailed on a disorderly conduct charge.

When the phone rings, Mom gets it. I hear her say, "Well, you'll have to ask him about that," and I assume it's for Dad. But instead she says, "Alec, it's a young lady calling for you."

"Hmm. Now who could that be?" Dad says without looking up from the sports page. I guess we both know. Girls aren't exactly lining up to call me. It has to be Mary Alice, and it is.

"Alec?" she says. "Would you like to come up and see a ball game Friday night?"

"Huh?" I answer. Where in Morrisonville am I goling to see a ball game at this time of year? What kind of a game? And why is Mary Alice inviting me?

"On television," she explains. "KPTV is going to do the Washington-Seattle game from Corvallis." Then she says "Huh?" and puts her hand over the receiver, and I'm left wondering what is going on.

"Dad says it's the first live telecast of a sporting event in Oregon," she announces when she comes back on the line. "Ron and Rob and I each get to invite one guest up to see it with us. I chose you. Can you come?"

"Oooh man! I'd sure like to. I'll ask Dad."

Dad looks thoughtful and jangles his ring of keys for several seconds when I tell him about it. Finally he says, "Let me speak to Mr. Patterson for a minute." I relay the request to Mary Alice, who puts her father on the line. Dad's end of the conversation consists mostly of , "Umm-humm…Yes…I see." Finally he says, "Well, I'll certainly let him come if he wishes to."

So it's set. I get to watch local television history being made, and I get to watch it with Mary Alice. Friday can't get here too soon for me. Of course I'm expecting the usual now-behave-yourself-and-act-like-a-gentleman lecture, but Dad gives me an extra helping of it right after dinner on Friday.

"Bud Patterson never does anything without a reason," he tells me. "There's something behind this invitation, and I'm not sure what it is. You can go, but be very, very careful up there, Alec."

"Dad, we're just going to watch a basketball game."

"I hope that's all there is to it, Son. But I have my doubts."

****

It's ironic, I guess, that the first live sports telecast from Oregon features two teams from Washington. What's even more strange is that the University of Washington and Seattle University have never played each other before, even though they're from the same city. The Huskies are part of the Pacific Coast Conference, while Seattle U. is a smaller school that has just made the jump to the big-college level for the 52-53 season.

Both teams, I learn from reading up on the game, have first-team all-Americans on their squads. Washington has Bob Houbergs, a six-seven center (and in 1953, six-seven is big), who tears Oregon apart in the game Dad and I listen to back in January. Seattle's Johnny O'Brian, is a five-nine guard who will probably set a single-season NCAA scoring record. His identical twin brother plays the other guard position.

The game is part of the NCAA tournament, which is still pretty low-key in 1953. March Madness, The Big Dance, The Sweet Sixteen, the Road to the Final Four—these terms won't be dreamed up for decades yet. But Oregon State College in Corvallis is one of four sites around the country where sixteen teams will be pared down to four over the course of two nights.

Mary Alice tells me that she'll come over with her brother Ron and his girlfriend to get me right after dinner. I'm ready to go and pacing the floor twenty minutes in advance.

"Remember what I told you!" Dad warns as he sees the car pull up in front.

Ron Patterson seems cool. He's a tall, lanky junior who plays forward on Morrisonville High's basketball team. He moves with the grace of a natural athlete and he smiles easily enough, but his face looks more like his mother's, and he does not have Mary Alice's big sad eyes.

"You and Sis can sit in the back," he says as he opens the door of an old Pontiac his Dad lets him drive. "But no monkey business, hear? I'm keeping an eye on both of you!"

"Aw, cut it out, Ron," his girlfriend says as she slides over next to him. "I think they're cute."

"You would!" he replies. But he laughs as he pops the clutch and peels away from the curb. Mary Alice and I keep two feet of space between us, but when I feel her hand brush against mine, I take it and she makes no objection.

But Dad's words have started me thinking. *Bud Patterson never does anything without a reason*. Why, when he has one of the very few television sets in town, is he using the game as a party for his kids instead of inviting his own friends? And why can they each invite only one guest? Why not let Ron invite his teammates over? He's the oldest, after all. As far as that goes, if they're so interested in the game, why not just get tickets for it? Corvallis is only forty miles away. Dad may be right. There *is* something strange about this.

"Alec, there's one thing I need to ask you," Mary Alice says as we start up The Hill. "You're not a Catholic, are you?"

"No. We're Presbyterians. Why?"

"Well, Seattle Univeristy is a Catholic School, and Dad—uh—"

"Dad can't stand mackerel-snappers!" Ron laughs as he finishes the sentence for her. "So make sure you root for the Huskies tonight, Alec. You too, Linda. He thinks

Episcopalians are almost as bad!" He slips an arm around his date and squeezes her. Linda giggles.

****

Mrs. Patterson is all smiles when she greets us, but the smiles look like they've been painted on. "So nice to see you again, Linda! And here's the young man who likes my cookies so much! I remember from last fall. There's another batch all ready, but you may have to fight Ron and Rob and Jim to get your share."

Jim turns out to be Rob's guest and one of his teammates on the junior high squad. "He's a starter," Mary Alice explains when we're alone together in the kitchen for a minute. "Rob's the last one off the bench. He wouldn't even be on the team if it weren't for Dad."

"What do you mean?"

"Dad made a deal with the coach. He'd buy new uniforms for the team if Rob could be on it and play a little. So he gets in for the last two minutes of the fourth quarter if they're way ahead or way behind. He doesn't even like the game, but Dad makes him play it."

"Why does he do that?" I ask.

"I guess it's because he's afraid Rob will turn out to be a sissy. Rob's really smart though, always gets straight A's. But it's a mean kind of smart. Watch out for him, Alec."

Rob Patterson might as well wear a sign saying, *Watch out for me—I'm bad!* He has the big eyes like Mary Alice, but his look even larger because the bottom half of his face is pinched in, almost like it had been squeezed in a vise. He doesn't look straight at you either. His gaze seems to slide off at an angle, as if he doesn't want you to know where he's really looking.

Maybe he's a decent-enough person if you really get to know him, but I'll bet that not many guys his age want to make the effort. I know not many my age would, including me. Perhaps Rob Patterson is a bit like Cap'n Andy—different and therefore scary.

Jim seems uneasy around him too. We sit around the television in the den and nibble from trays of snacks while we wait for the game to start. Suddenly Mr. Patterson asks me, "Alec, who are you going to root for?"

I'm tempted to say Seattle, just to see what kind of a reaction I would get. But I catch the pleading look in Mary Alice's eyes and say, "The Huskies, Mr. Patterson."

"Why?" he demands.

"Well—" I think as fast as I can. "My favorite team is Oregon State, but if the Beavers can't be in it, then I'd like someone they've played to take it." (I really am an Oregon State fan, mainly because Mom and Dad went to Oregon and it bothers them just a bit to have me root for their rivals.) "We almost beat the Huskies once," I add, hoping I remember correctly or that Bud Patterson doesn't know either.

Apparently he's satisfied, because he turns to Jim and asks him the same question. Jim shrugs. "Doesn't really matter to me," he says. "If you guys want the Huskies, I'll go for them too."

"Well, *I'll* go with the Chiefs," Linda states before she's even asked. Mr. Patterson sends a glare of pure malice her way. But before he can say anything, Rob chimes in.

"I think I will too," he says in an offhand but very deliberate way.

"Don't bet money on it, Little Brother," Ron cautions. "Washington has the height and the depth. It'll be over by the third quarter."

We turn our attention to the set as the starting lineups are introduced. All the players on both teams are white, of course, since this is the Pacific Northwest in 1953. KPTV only has two cameras to cover the game. One shoots the action on the court from high overhead, while the second, at floor level, shows closeups of the coaches and players on the bench. After one minor problem with the sound, the game begins. Ron is quickly proved right.

Seattle is small and quick, but they have no answer for Houbergs. The Washington center hooks over the smaller defenders or grabs offensive rebounds and puts them back. Desperately, Seattle rushes in a reserve who's six-eight, but he's also slow and clumsy. If he plays back, he can't defend against the hook. If he moves up, Houbergs spins around him for an easy layin and usually draws a foul when he does.

Johnny O'Brian tries his best to answer and does drop in several long set shots. He's also deadly from the free-throw line. With a three-point arc to shoot from, O'Brian might make the game interesting. But there is no three-point shot in 1953, and Washington steadily pulls away.

I get so caught up in the flow of the game and the magic of watching a live telecast that I don't even notice the level of tension in the den until just before halftime. KPTV cuts to a floor shot showing a priest sitting next to the coach on the Seattle bench. Both look resigned to the fact that they're in over their heads. Bud Patterson lets loose with an explosive chortle.

"Okay, Padre! Give them doggone mackerel-snappers their last rites or whatever the Sam Hill you call it. The Huskies are going to bury 'em!"

Mrs. Patterson shoots him a look and shakes her head, but her husband ignores it. By halftime he's jubilant, but it's not a kind of happiness I want to share in.

He disappears for several minutes at during the break, and Mrs. Patterson brings in another tray of snacks for us. Mary Alice looks like she's ready to cry again, so I move over next to her and tell her how much I'm enjoying the game and how great it is that she invites me to see it. She tries to smile, but doesn't quite bring it off.

"Alec, I'm really sorry about…all this," she says as she moves a little closer.

"Hey you two! No cuddling in the den during the game!" Bud Patterson practically bellows this from the doorway.

"Ron! Rob! Keep an eye on your sister!" He mutters something else I can't hear, and maybe that's just as well. His face is flushed and his large eyes seem almost unnaturally bright.

Bud Patterson and his daughter have the same kind of eyes, and yet they don't. With Mary Alice, it's like you're looking into a deep pool. It's almost like you can see all the way through to her soul. But with her father—the only thing I can think of is being in a barber's chair with big mirrors in front of you and behind you. You see the same image repeated on and on into infinity, and it's not a very pretty image either.

The game's outcome is obvious by the middle of the third quarter. Washington wins, 92-70. Houbergs scores 45 points, almost half the Huskies' total. Johnny O'Brian ends up with 25 for Seattle. Bud Patterson lets loose a whoop as the final buzzer sounds.

"I guess we showed them candle-burning mackerel-snappers this time!" he guffaws. "Aren't you sorry you picked 'em?" he asks Linda and Rob.

"Dad, it's only a game," Ron says as he puts a protective arm around Linda.

"No, Son! You're wrong! It's never just a game when you're playing *those* people!"

I come away from that evening with a sour taste in my mouth. Bud Batterson needles Rob and Linda unmercifully. Jim is ignored and so are Mary Alice and myself, after that one outburst. Why is he doing this? Why is a successful businessman acting like such a jerk?

The ride home is quiet. Linda looks ready to break into tears, and Ron's knuckles are white against the steering wheel. Mary Alice takes my hand and gives it a squeeze, as if to say she's sorry she brought me into this. I squeeze back and whisper, "It's all right." I'll get some answers from her, but I'll wait until Monday to do it.

There's a second game following Washington-Seattle U., but it's not televised. Santa Clara beats Wyoming. On Saturday Houbergs cans another 34 points as Washington tops Santa Clara, 74-62. In the consolation game Seattle takes care of Wyoming, 80-64. Johnny O'Brian gets 30 and sets an NCAA single-season scoring record with 916 points. I hope Bud Patterson reads that, and I hope it gives him indigestion.

****

On Monday J. P. tells me to ride with Pietrowski and then do his route for the next three days. Pete's grandmother has died up in Wenatchee, and it will take the family three days to go up, attend the funeral and come back. Pete just shrugs when I tell him I'm sorry to hear that she died.

"Hey, she was eighty and had two heart attacks this past year. We knew it was just a matter of time. At least it didn't happen next week and foul up spring vacation."

Paul Reed is the one who takes the news hard. "You're lucky in a way," he tells Pietrowski. "You don't live with her every day. If something happened to Gams, I don't know what me and Binky would do. She and Gump are all we've got."

"You still don't know what happened to your folks?" Pete asks.

"Gams says she'll tell us when Binky turns eighteen. Shoot! I'll be twenty then."

"Yeah, but suppose they die before then?" Archer puts in.

"Gams says she's got a letter written up that explains everything, but it's in a safe-deposit box and it can't come out till Binky is eighteen."

After Pietrowski and I finish his route, I swing by the library to see Mary Alice. Her eyes are red and I can't tell if she's happy to see me or not. Mrs. Carruthers lets us go into the back room again to talk.

"When I saw John bring the paper in by himself, I thought you were still mad at us," she says. I explain about Pietrowski's emergency and she seems relieved. But I'm not.

"What was that all about Friday night?" I ask her. "Does your dad always act that way when you have company?"

"I—I think it was because we were going to have the Cloningers over. You know, the bank president. I think Dad is trying to work out some kind of deal with him. But they got tickets at the last minute and decided to go down to Corvallis and see the game in person. I know Dad was awful upset about it."

"Yeah, but why did he make all those remarks about Catholics? The Cloningers aren't Catholic, are they?" I remember J. P. chewing me out for calling Officer Derflinger Old Dirty Fingers. If that could get back to him, then surely Bud Patterson's remarks could find their way to someone at St. James.

"Alec, he'd been drinking. Couldn't you tell?"

No, I couldn't. I see Mom and Dad have one highball on Friday night to celebrate the end of the week, and they have champagne on New Years Eve—which is when Aunt Emma gets so bombed she can't see straight. But that's the sum total of my experience with people drinking.

"Does this happen often?" I ask.

"It didn't used to, but it's getting to where it does. He always feels terrible afterwards. Saturday morning he called us in one at a time and apologized to us. He told me to tell you he's sorry if he hurt your feelings too. He said he'd never mean to hurt me. He'd never raise his hand to me. He never has. I almost wish he would."

"You'd *want* him to hurt you?"

"No. He's never been mean like that. He's never slapped me or spanked me. Never even shaken me."

"I know some kids who'd be grateful for that."

She looks at me and slowly shakes her head. "He never hugs me anymore either. Does your dad still hug you?"

"Yes," I admit. "He does."
"Then you're lucky!"

****

That night I lie awake and think about what Mary Alice says. Never hit, slapped or spanked, but never hugged either. I can only remember really being paddled once, when I'm about five and swipe my dad's favorite briar pipe to blow soap bubbles and then try to lie my way out of it. After warming my bottom good and proper, he tells me, "If you'd 'fessed up, you would have gotten off with one or two swats. All the rest were for lying. You can make mistakes, and you can get yourself in trouble. Lord knows I did when I was a kid. But don't you ever, *ever* lie to me!"

I haven't lied to Dad since, though I do sometimes keep part of the truth back. It works for me. I get off with a lecture and a warning after my intimate encounter with Sandy Evans. She doesn't and has never liked me since. This year Dad even drops his if-you-ever-get-a-licking-at-school threat. But I still get hugs every night from both Mom and Dad, and I know they both love me. Mary Alice may live in a big house on top of The Hill, with two or three cars and a big console television, but I think I have the better home.

Spring vacation starts right after school on Friday the 20th. I meet Mary Alice at the library and ask her what her plans for the week are.

"We're leaving for Denver tomorrow," she says.

"You're going to drive all the way to Colorado and back in one week?"

"No, Silly. We're going to fly! Dad has business in Denver, and he's taking Mom and Ron and Rob and me along. He's renting a car for us when we get there, so we can see the sights while he works."

Wow! Flying in 1953—something only the rich can afford to do. It's glamorous. It's expensive. And it's dangerous or so it seems. I don't cut out articles about plane crashes, but there seems to be one every month or so. Of course, these are smaller planes, so the death toll seldom goes beyond 40 or 50. Still, would I want to go up in one of those things and fly halfway across the country?

You bet I would! Mary Alice Patterson is one lucky dog—or so I think in the spring of 1953.

****

During the last half of March Dad has me cut out and save two sports articles for my journal. On March 18 the National League unanimously votes to let the Boston Braves move their team to Milwaukee. This is the first move of a major league franchise in fifty years. Others will soon follow. "They'll come west to California, Alec," Dad tells me. "It will mean the end of the Pacific Coast League as we know it."

The second article concerns the death of Jim Thorpe, who is considered the greatest athlete of the first half of the twentieth century. I don't give it too much attention, because right at that time the Crossman Case hits the news.

Chad Crossman uses a hunting knife to stab his father and stepmother to death in their sleep on a farm in Eastern Oregon. Then he takes off, but gets only five or six miles before he is caught. It's just another ugly little murder case, except for one thing.

Chad Crossman is eleven years old. He's *my* age.

On March 26 the *Journal* runs a picture and description of him on the front page. He stands four-eleven and weighs eighty-five pounds. *I'm almost exactly the same size!* The reporters describe him as "dazed and confused." So am I.

Something is horribly wrong. Kids my age don't do things like that—at least, not in 1953. Sure, I get in a few fights with other boys, but always just with bare hands, and the worst I ever receive or give is a bloody nose. Sure, I argue with Mom and Dad, but we never raise a hand against each other. For the first time I see evil touch someone my own age. What pushes Chad Crossman into an act so terrible?

Well, we don't find out—not in 1953, at any rate. A grand jury refuses to indict him as an adult, so he's turned over to the head-doctors for a year of "study and evaluation"—whatever that is supposed to mean.

(Okay, Chad Crossman is not the guy's real name. He's my age and probably still alive, and I have no wish to wreck his life a second time. But check the *Journal* and *Oregonian* archives for March of 1953, and you'll find the stories splashed all over the front pages.)

When I ask Dad for his opinion, he can only shake his head. "There's a lot of evil in this world, Son," he says, "and you can never tell where it will turn up."

"But remember this, Alec," Mom says. "For every Chad Crossman there are thousands of boys like you. The good always outnumber the bad, and that's why we have a civilization."

****

On Monday the 30th we go back to school. The *Journal*'s lead headline that night reads, *New Red Bid Raises Hope for War's End*. It's a false hope, and the war drags on.

I'm doing Madigan's route solo now while he learns Scott's. There's no official pay yet, although J. P. slips me a quarter and buys me a pepsi. But the big day is almost here. On Wednesday Route 3 will be mine all mine!

Mary Alice is absent from school, but she's there at the library when I come by with the paper. "Stop in on your way home. She needs to talk with you," Mrs. Carruthers tells me. When I return, she gestures toward the back room.

"Be careful," Mrs. Carruthers warns. "Something has upset her terribly."

I can tell Mary Alice has been crying, but she's stopped, so I don't try to use my snotty handkerchief again. Instead I say the first dumb thing that pops into my head.

"Well, how was Denver?"

"Alec!" she wails as she bursts into tears. "We all have to move there right after school's out!"

Chapter Eight:Route 3

W*ednesday, April 1, 1953:*The big day is finally here! So what if it's April Fools? I'm an official *Oregon Journal* carrier now. I cut straight for home as school lets out, check in with Mom and then ride for Benny's as fast as I can. There's a stack of forty papers waiting for me in that back room, and from now on the card in that stack will say *Lewis*!

And there is business to transact with Ken Scott, who is now officially off the roster of carriers. We have a little ceremony in the back room, and I buy his double bags for two dollars, which is probably more than they're worth. I could order new ones for three dollars, but I like Ken's. They're a bit faded and stained, but they make me feel like a veteran. That's important when you're the baby of the bunch.

J.P. buys Ken his last official Pepsi. Mrs. Benson adds a free candy bar, and Jill gets all teary when she jumps on his back.

"Promise you'll come back and see us, Kenny!" she begs.

"Twerp, you are determined to give me a hernia, aren't you?" he says as he pries her off. "All right, I will—*if* you'llbe nice to Alec."

"Uck!" she says.

"All right then, halfway nice."

"Well,okay. But only because you asked."

ROUTE THREE

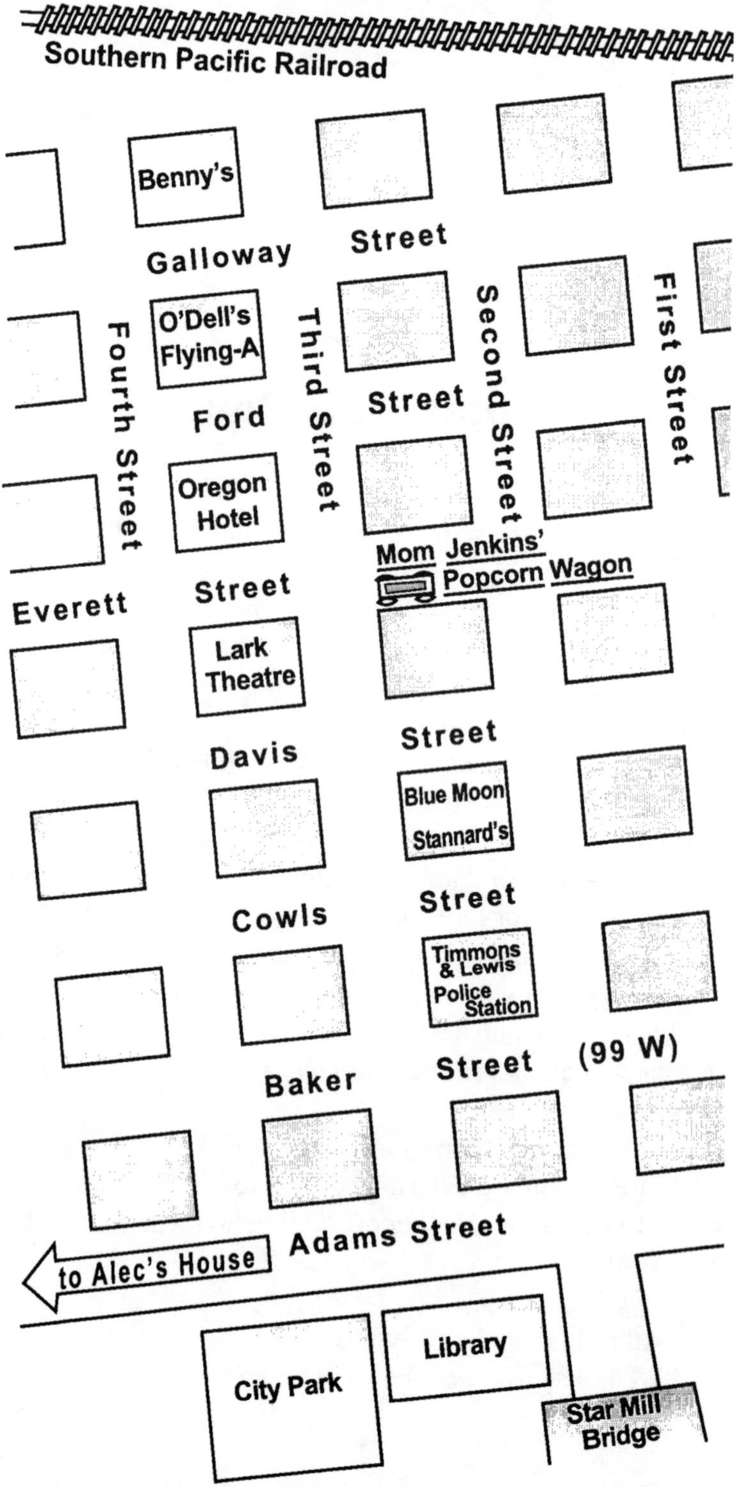

Southern Pacific Railroad

Benny's

Galloway Street

O'Dell's Flying-A

Fourth Street

Third Street

Second Street

First Street

Ford Street

Oregon Hotel

Mom Jenkins' Popcorn Wagon

Everett Street

Lark Theatre

Davis Street

Blue Moon

Stannard's

Cowls Street

Timmons & Lewis

Police Station

Baker Street (99 W)

to Alec's House

Adams Street

Library

City Park

Star Mill Bridge

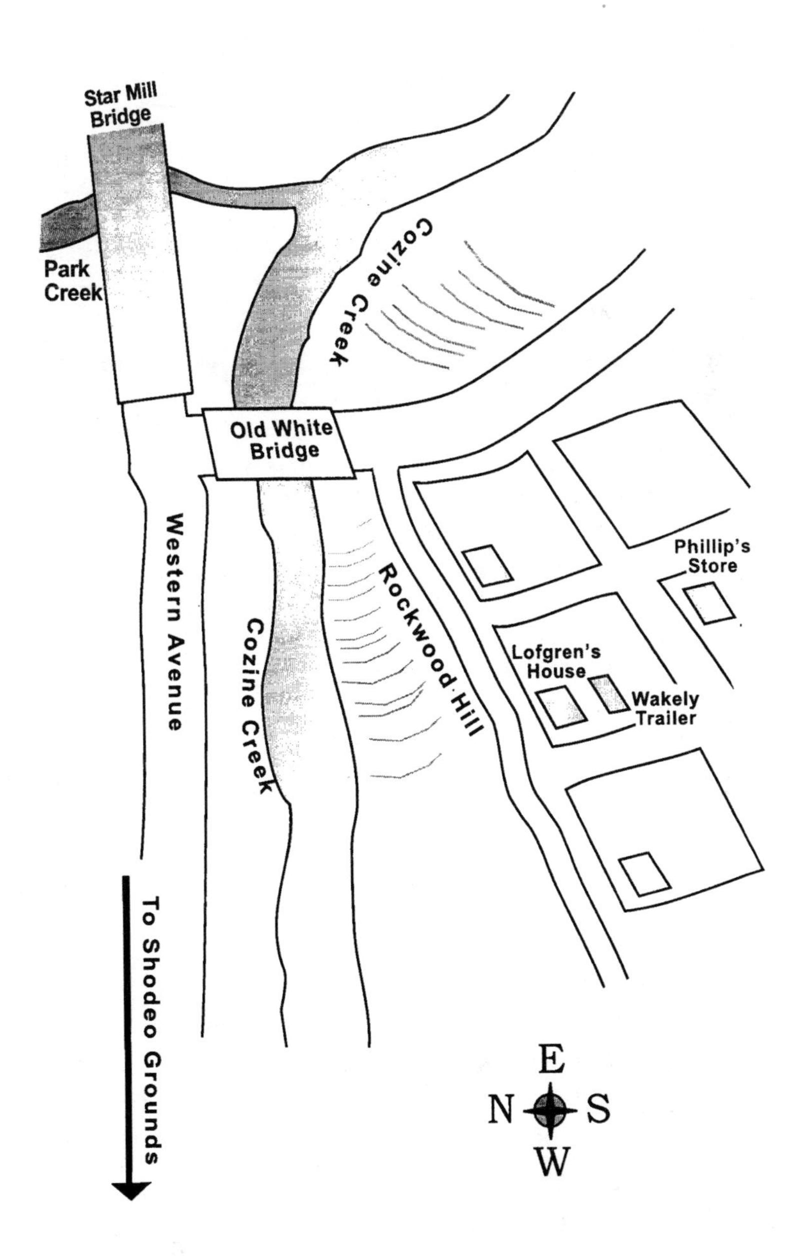
Star Mill Bridge
Park Creek
Cozine Creek
Old White Bridge
Western Avenue
Cozine Creek
Rockwood Hill
Phillip's Store
Lofgren's House
Wakely Trailer
To Shodeo Grounds
E
N
S
W

Jill follows Ken out to the front, and Archer, who has the stack next to mine, leans over and mutters, "Hey Lewis, you know the difference between a tavern and an elephant's fart?"

"Nope," I answer as I shake my head and grin.

"Well, one is a barroom and the other's a bar—OOM! Get it?"

I know I'm one of the gang now. Dirty Dave has told me a joke.

****

It's a cloudy afternoon, but the rain is holding off, for the moment at least. I tie the bags on the carrier without pulling the rain flaps down and begin delivering Route 3—*my* route now! First comes the Parker House just across the Southern Pacific tracks, then I reverse and head west down Third Street. I'm carrying almost half the papers flat, since many deliveries are to shops and apartments.

Two customers in Frank & Don's Barber Shop debate the merits of the Yankees and the Dodgers (who in 1953 are still in Brooklyn). "Don't count Cleveland out," I hear Frank warn them. "Not with their pitching. Feller and Lemon could win twenty apiece."

I wait for a lull and say, "'Afternoon, Mr. Lucas. Madigan will be in to collect later on, but I'll be delivering the paper now."

"That's fine, Alec. Give it to Old Bradshaw there." I pass through a connecting door into the Yamhill Hotel and leave another paper at the front desk. Then I'm off across the street to one of my favorite places, Mom Jenkins' Popcorn Wagon—a pre-World War I auto up on blocks and painted like a circus wagon. I wait until she deals with a customer, then hand her the paper and wish her a good afternoon.

"A quick smile and a friendly word will cost you maybe a couple of seconds, but the dividends they can pay are enormous." Dad keeps harping on this every day.

"Remember, no one *has* to take the paper from you. They'll do it because they want to, and the main reason they'll want to is because they like you. So mind your manners and watch your step every second you're out there."

I scramble up flights of old wooden stairs to get the apartments over the stores. *Who are these people?* I'll find out when I collect next month. Officer Derflinger is behind the desk at the police station when I bring their paper in. I'm trying to think of him now as Officer D and not Old Dirty Fingers. "Hey Derf!" a voice calls from behind the barred door of the one-cell jail next to the office. "Can I see the funnies when you're done?"

"You can have 'em now, Oscar," Officer D says as he rolls a section and slides it between the bars. "All I want is the sports page."

Back to Third to get the Blue Moon and Stannard's grocery next door. *Wow! Bet I'm the only 11-year-old in town who gets to walk into a bar by himself every day!* Stannards delivers groceries to Mom three or four times a week, so Old Man Stannard, if he's behind the counter, will slice a sliver of cheese off the big wheel they keep on a table near the door or dip me out some peanut butter from the barrel on the counter. Today it's a dollop of peanut butter, freshly made this morning, on a piece of wax paper. Why buy the stuff in jars when you can get it fresh?

At the library I hand a flat paper to Mrs. Carruthers, then throw triangles to three houses on the other side of Second Street. *Only three out of eight. Not good. I'll have to try to get the others.*

Second Street is a hill leading down to the Star Mill Bridge. I pull out of the last driveway and head back up the hill to get a good flying start, then turn and pump the pedals on the old Columbia for all I'm worth and rip onto the Star Mill at a hundred miles an hour. (Okay, maybe a little over twenty on a good day.)

Two reasons for this. First of all, it's fun. Secondly, if I can hit the turn onto the old white bridge over Cozine Creek at full speed, the momentum may get me all the way up Rockwood Hill without having to get off and walk the last few yards. Rockwood is shorter but steeper than The Hill where Mary Alice lives with her brand-new English 3-speed. My heavy old Columbia takes the turn easily enough, but starts to slow almost immediately. I'm pumping for all I'm worth before I even hit the end of the bridge.

Drive! Drive! Drive! You can do it! But the old Columbia slows and, twenty yards from the top, starts to wobble. I have to get off and walk it. Another case of almost, but not quite. On a 3-speed I probably could do it easily. Maybe someday I can get one. Maybe someday I can get a lot of things. Maybe...

All but two of the streets on Rockwood Hill are gravel and mud—mostly mud at this time of year. As I stuff a paper into a tube under a mailbox, someone calls "Arric!" That's Cap'n Andy, and *Arric* is as close as he can come to *Alec.* "Where paper?" he demands. His voice reminds me of a load of gravel sliding down a metal roof, and he's become the Morrisonville bogeyman now that Joseph Stalin is dead.

"Oh yes," I say as calmly as I can. "I've got it right here for you." I dig out a copy of yesterday's paper and hand it over.

"Not folded!" he complains, so I have to get off my bike, lay the day-old *Journal* in the gravel and mud and fold it into a triangle. It pretty well ruins the paper for reading, but I doubt if Cap'n Andy reads it anyway.

Yet for some reason I'm not afraid of him. I've never been this close, near enough to tell he has bad breath and b.o., yet there's something about him that reassures me and says that I'm safe as long as I treat him kindly.

"Would you like me to show you how to fold them sometime?" I ask.

He ponders the question for several seconds while I study his face. His eyes are as black as two chunks of ebony, and the brows grow together over the bridge of his nose, which has been broken at least once and probably several times. I can hear a whispering note, almost a whistle, when he exhales. One front tooth is black, two more are yellow and two more are gone. Someone in his past has slashed him across his lower lip, because I see a scar running all the way down past one corner of this mouth.

Cap'n Andy stands barely five feet, maybe an inch taller than I am. But he must be double my weight and, from a glance at the muscle in his arms and neck, very little of it is fat. I notice that he could also use a shave as well as a bath.

Yet when he smiles, which probably isn't often, the eyes appear to lighten and the scar seems to fade. "That nice, Arric. Thanka," he says and trots off down the street with his paper. He's not riding his old black bicycle, so he must live somewhere close by.

Two other Rockwood Hill residents will play big roles in my life during this year of 1953, and I'm attracted to them almost immediately. The first is Mr. Lofgren, who takes the daily and my one bulldog and sits on his front porch every afternoon waiting for me to come by.

"'Afternoon there—Alec, isn't it?" Once again I hear that Southern Plains twang, though softer this time. He's been here a while, but I'd bet he comes from Oklahoma or Texas. His age? That could be anywhere from 45 to 65, but he looks like he's lived a rough life.

"Yessir. That's right. Here's your paper."

"Good! I always gotta read the funnies first," he admits. "Read every one every day in both papers. You read 'em too?"

"Some. Not all. What's your favorite?"

"*Dick Tracy* in *The Oregonian* and *Kerry Drake* in the *Journal*. What about you?"

"*Hopalong Cassidy,*" I answer. "It's on television too, but we can't pick up KPTV down where I live."

"Bet we could get it up here, but I don't think nobody on Rockwood has a set. Too dang expensive. This ain't exactly the richest part of town."

"Your house looks pretty nice," I tell him. It does too. Nothing fancy about it, but the paint looks new, the lawn is trimmed and someone, probably his wife, has planted flowers around the borders. The only thing out of place is an old trailer, a real junker, that I see in one corner of his back yard.

"That's what we lived in when we first come up to Oregon 'bout ten-eleven years ago," he says as he notices me staring at it. "We was nothin' but fruit-pickin', dust-bowl Okies back then. Can you still hear it in my voice?"

"Just a little."

"Yeah. I reckon all this Oregon rain's softened it up a mite. When me and Clara came up here to work in the Portland shipyards durin' the war, we lived in that ol' heap and made do till afterward, when I got me a job down here with Ol' Man Crockett who ran the bakery. When he died, I got to take it over. Left me this house too. His wife had already passed, and they never had any kids. So, you wanta guess why I still keep that ol' pile of junk?"

"No. Why?"

"Well, me and Clara was lucky. The war got us outa the migrant life. But there's others that want out now, only they ain't got no place to stay till they find steady work. So, if I like the looks of 'em, I let 'em stay there for two-three months till they can afford to get a place of their own. Ain't nobody in there now, but there most likely will be, come fall."

As we talk, I realize two things. First, Mr. Lofgren is not talking down to me, like a grownup does to a kid. This is man-to-man, one working guy to another. Second, Mr. Lofgren must have led quite a life. Somebody ought to write about it. Maybe, someday, I can. People don't have to be famous to be interesting, I realize. There are stories all around me, and all I have to do is collect them.

Two streets down and one over from Mr. Lofgren is Mrs. Phillips, who has the only store on Rockwood Hill. It's just a garage that someone has converted into a tiny grocery shop. Mrs. Phillips herself is a slightly larger model of Mrs. Chivington, my third-grade teacher. A little bell over the door jangles when I walk in and set her paper on the counter by the cash register.

"'Afternoon, Mrs. Phillips. How's business?"

"Well, I won't starve for a little while yet," she always says as she looks up from her knitting. I know she's a widow with twelve or maybe thirteen grandchildren, and she keeps the shop mainly to give her something to do and a chance to visit with neighbors when they drop in for one or two items—things they suddenly discover they need, but which aren't worth a trip all the way into town. She carries one item that I always like.

"Got any more of those big blue jawbreakers?" I ask.

"The supply man was supposed to bring 'em today, but he hasn't showed up yet. I'm afraid little places like mine aren't very high on his list. How's John doing?"

"Just fine. His new route has sixty-five dailies and sixty-seven Sundays."

"And they stuck you up here with us, didn't they?"

"I don't mind. It's a good place to start. And there's some nice folks up here, like you and Mr. Lofgren. I even talked with Cap'n Andy this afternoon."

"That's not his real name, Alec,"

"I know. But I don't know what his real name is."

"Bertram Slade. He doesn't like it, though. Especially the first name. You remember when he got in trouble for chasing after those girls last year?"

"Yeah. They talked to us at school about it."

"Well, it all happened when they snuck up behind him when he stopped in front of the library. I think one girl dared the other, but they both yelled, 'Bertram Slade is a crazy old maid!' That's what set him off. He's really not bad. He just can't stand being teased. It's a good thing for them he can't run very fast."

****

Even though we're now in the last quarter of the fifth grade, Mrs. Foster still reads to us for twenty minutes right after we come in from noon recess. She says it calms us down and puts us in a good mood to study. Maybe it does. None of us will admit it, but we still like to be read to, and Mrs. Foster has a good voice and knows how to use it.

For the past seven or eight days she's been reading from *Gettysburg* by MacKinley Kantor, a Landmark Book about the great Civil War battle. On this Friday she ends her reading with the episode of Wesley Culp, the grandson of the man for whom Culp's Hill is named. Wesley Culp goes south as a young man and returns as a Confederate soldier, only to be killed while attacking Culp's Hill.

"So," she says as she closes the book. "This is what we call irony. To leave your homeland, come back as part of an invading army, and then be killed right next to the very house where you had been born. Think about that."

I steal a quick glance at Mary Alice and, sure enough, I can see tears, though she doesn't actually cry. I think, *what is wrong with her? Gettysburg is ninety years in the past, and there's barely a handful of Civil War veterans left alive.* (By the end of the year there will be two, one Yank and one Reb.)

Words like "oversensitive" and "vulnerability" aren't used much in 1953, and certainly not by fifth-graders. The other girls dismiss Mary Alice as a weirdo. The boys, except for me, probably don't think about her at all. But all the while I'm watching her, I'm thinking, *what makes her that way? What makes any of us do the things we do? Could I ever find out?*

At Benny's after school, I glance at the main headline as I fold my papers, and I read, *Ex-Officer Admits Spying For Russia*. Jeez Lou*eeze*! That's worse than Wesley Culp attacking his birthplace! It's maybe even worse than Chad Crossman stabbing his father to death! How can a man betray his own country. Yeah, I hope the dirty rat gets the sizzle-seat, *but what makes someone do things like that?*

After finishing the route, I double back to the library. Mary Alice is shelving books again, but Mrs. Carruthers tells her she can go down to the swings with me for a little while if she wants. "Just be back before five," she cautions. Mary Alice has a watch and I don't, so I glance at the clock over the front desk and see that we'll have about twenty minutes.

The afternoon is cloudy with just a hint of drizzle and cold enough to make me keep my jacket zipped. We have the whole play area to ourselves, so we sit facing each other in a covered platform double swing and push with our feet to get it rocking. When we're going pretty good, I ask her, "Why did you get all teary over the story of Wesley Culp? It happened ninety years ago." I'm normally not a nosy guy, but I want to know why people do things. I can't ask Wesley Culp or Chad Crossman or the officer who spies against his own country, but I can ask Mary Alice.

"I can't help it," she answers me. "It's so sad to think of him coming all that way and then dying just as he reaches home again."

"But he was a Reb! He was attacking his home!"

"I know that, Alec, but still…". She leaves it unfinished and we rock silently for several seconds until I try again.

"Why is your dad moving you all to Denver?"

"It's a chance for him to take over one of the biggest dealerships in the West, he says. And he can send us all to private schools in Denver. The only ones we have here are St. James and that dinky little thing the Seventh-Day Adventists run."

"Do you want to go to a private school?"

"I don't really care. I don't think I'd mind St. James. I don't think there's really anything wrong with Catholics. They worship the same God we do."

"Then why does your dad hate them?"

She shakes her head, but says nothing. I hear a giggle and see a boy and girl walk past us, holding hands, on a path about ten yards away. They're maybe fifteen or sixteen, and I hear the boy say, "Dang little kids got the swing. Guess we'll have to go down across the creek." The girl giggles again, and they continue down the path toward the bottom level of the park.

Mary Alice and I both know where they're going. Just beyond the footbridge spanning the tiny creek that flows through the bottom level of the park and passes under the Star Mill Bridge to join Cozine Creek a hundred yards or so to the south, the park slopes up again, and that slope is thick with trees and shrubs. It's where the teenagers who don't have cars yet go to make out. I wait until they're out of earshot, then ask Mary Alice, "You wanta follow 'em and watch?"

"No, Alec. That's mean!"

Then, before I realize what I'm saying, I blurt out, "Would you just go down there with me then?"

She shakes her head again, but more in sadness than in anger. "I can't," she says. "I'm not even supposed to be here with you."

"Then why *are* you here with me?"

She ducks her head as she tries to find the right words. "Because I like to be with you." She looks up, blushes and tries a smile, but it doesn't quite come off.

"Then talk to me. Tell me why your dad hates Catholics."

Again she is silent and we rock back and forth for several seconds. Finally I give the slats an extra hard push and nearly throw her off balance. "Why?" I repeat.

"I don't know for sure," she says. "I think his father, Grandpa Patterson, may have made him feel that way."

"What was he like?"

"I can't remember him. He died when I was one or two. Ron can remember him a little. Says he had an awful temper. Even Dad was afraid of him."

"Yeah," I persist. "But what does that have to do with hating Catholics?"

"I—I'm not supposed to talk about it," she says. "It's kind of a family secret."

Okay, I know all about those. Mom and Dad have warned me many times never to say a word about Aunt Emma Snyder's New Years Eve binges. Yet whatever Mary Alice's dirty little family secret is, her dad has hurt people with it, including me. So I make Mary Alice an offer.

"If you tell me, I promise not to tell my folks or anyone else," I say. She shakes her head again. "Okay then," I offer. "I'll trade secrets with you—one of ours for one of yours. I'll even go first." For some reason this reminds me of negotiating with Sandy Evans out behind her dad's garage, only back then I'm the reluctant one.

"Well..." She hesitates and I press her.

"Look around. There's only you and me. No one else can hear us."

"Okay," she finally says. "But only if you go first."

Which is exactly what I say to Sandy back in 1947.

So I tell her all about Aunt Emma and her New Years Eve visits, including quoting from the Book of Proverbs with a terrible hangover the next morning and preaching against strong drink the next week. I even tell Mary Alice about the journal Aunt Emma has me keep. "Okay," I say as I finish up. "Now it's your turn."

"Promise me you won't write it in your journal?" she asks, and I promise not to. (But I don't promise not to remember it.) She takes a deep breath and then tells me everything she knows about her grandfather.

Apparently the old man was one of the founders of the Ku Klux Klan in Oregon back in the early 1920's. This really jolts me, since these guys are supposed to be a handful of dangerous idiots down South who dress up in white sheets and run around terrorizing Negroes when they try to register to vote. There are very few Negroes in Oregon in 1953 and practically none outside of Portland. There must have been even fewer back in the 1920's. So I ask her whom the Klan went after.

"Catholics," she says. "Foreigners too—and Jews, of course. But there weren't many of them around. "Do you know they once got the legislature to pass a bill outlawing Catholic schools in Oregon?"

That's news to me. Yes, we study Oregon History back in the fourth grade, but it's a sanitized version that doesn't go past the nineteenth century. I read about Lewis & Clark, Dr. John McLoughlin and the Hudson's Bay Company, Jason Lee and the Methodist Mission. I even remember that Abraham Lincoln turns down the chance to be Oregon's first territorial governor in 1849. But the uglier parts of our history are quietly swept under the rug.

"Of course, the courts threw the law out," she adds. "Then there was some scandal, and the whole Klan just kind of folded up and melted away."

"But why did your grandpa start hating Catholics in the first place?"

"I think it was Uncle Quentin's death. His guns jammed in combat, and Dad says Grandpa told him it was because his mechanic didn't load them properly. He was trying to clear them when a German fighter got behind him and shot him down."

"I still don't see the connection."

"Well, the mechanic was French, and the French are Catholics."

"That's stupid!" I tell her. "Wouldn't it make more sense to hate Germans? It was a German who killed your uncle, after all."

"I think Uncle Quentin's death made Grandpa a little crazy. Apparently they couldn't get along, and Uncle Quentin ran off to join the war without getting Grandpa's permission first. Of course he was old enough that he didn't need it, but

I guess it really hurt Grandpa that he didn't ask. Then, when he was killed, Grandpa had to find someone to blame so he wouldn't have to blame himself. So he told Dad and the other kids how the very people Uncle Quentin went to help got him killed, and that they were all Catholics, and all Catholics were like that and would stab you in the back whenever they got the chance.

"And your dad believed it?"

"Alec, do you believe the things your dad tells you?"

"Yeah, but he'd never tell me a lie like that."

"How can you be sure?" she challenges, and I'm stumped for an answer. "Sometimes I don't know what to believe," she continues. "All I know for sure is that Uncle Quentin was a brave man, and I wish I'd got the chance to know him."

Her eyes start to tear up again, so she looks at her watch. "It's five already," she tells me. "We've got to get back."

We walk slowly back to the library without holding hands, without even touching each other. The enormity of what we have both done is slowly sinking in. We have each broken our word and betrayed a family secret. We probably look guiltier than if we had walked down across the creek together.

Chapter Nine: Lovebird

April slowly drifts toward May, the last full month of the school year. The weather gradually turns warmer, but not much dryer. The war in Korea drags on. Peace seems like a mirage—now it's almost within reach, and now it's gone again.

On a Saturday morning in late April, J. P. asks me if I'd like to go with him and a couple other carriers to work the move list Monday night.

"What's that?" I ask, and he explains that every Monday afternoon he gets a list from the city water and light department of everyone who has moved into or out of town or moved to another house within the city during the past week.

"It's a blast," Rush tells me. "We take turns calling on the move-ins and try to get 'em to take the paper. If we sign some up, J. P. treats us afterward. Plus you get credit for the orders too. You can get all kinds of stuff."

"Such as?"

"Well, you want a new front bag? Get three full orders, and you get it free."

So, Monday night at 6:45, I'm ready when J, P.'s old Chevy pulls up in front of the house and honks. Pat Rush is in the front seat, so I pile in the back seat with Joe Ferraday, a tall, skinny blonde kid who has the route on the far north end of town. J. P. says, "All right, we're ready to go now," as he flips on the overhead light to check the list. I peer over the top of the seat to study it with him.

It's a sheet of yellow paper, divided into three columns headed *Name, From* and *To*. There are twelve to fifteen listings, but three in the *To* column are blank, meaning they've moved out of town. Six or seven more are moves within town. J. P. crosses three of them off. "They already take the paper, and we've done the transfers," he tells us. He indicates four names where the *From* column is blank. "We'll try these first."

We find the first house and Ferraday leads off. It's an older place with a big porch. He knocks, a light comes on and we see the door open. "Uh oh!" Rush mutters. "A woman—not good."

"Why not?" I ask.

"They won't make a decision. You go through the whole song-and-dance and they just turn and yell, 'Hey Mike! We wanna take the *Journal*?' and he'll say, 'Naw, I don't think so.' Just wait. The best he'll do is a callback."

Ferraday comes back shaking his head. "They want *The Oregonian*. Wouldn't ya know?"

"But they haven't got it yet," J. P. says. "Take 'em an extra tomorrow, Joe. It's not far off your route. Tell 'em we'll give 'em one till *The Oregonian* comes. They may just change their minds." Ferraday looks doubtful, but he agrees.

The next house is in the newer part of town. Rush looks at it and grins. "I like this one," he says. "Watch close, Alec. I'll show you how it's done."

He knocks and a porch light comes on. The door opens and a man appears. "He got the husband," Ferraday mutters. "Lucky!"

The door opens wider and Rush steps inside. "Got 'em!" J. P. says. Two minutes later Rush runs back waving a white order pad.

"Daily and Sunday!" he cries as he peels off the top sheet and hands it over. "Told you it looked good."

Now it's my turn. We head across town to an address out by the college, but when we find the house, all the lights are out. "That's okay," J. P. says. "That's Reed's route. I'll have him call on 'em tomorrow. Alec, let's see if we can find you someone at home."

We make for the last of the four houses that don't show a moving address from somewhere in town. The lights are on. Rush opens the door and I slide out. "Remember what you're gonna say?" J. P. asks and I nod. "Then go get 'em!" he tells me.

Am I nervous? Oh man! Yes I am. I'm going up to a strange house to try to convince a strange adult to subscribe to a paper I've been delivering, officially, for less than a month. Suppose I forget what to say? This is not like the girl scouts out selling their cookies door to door. They can rely on being cute, and I sure can't do that. Is this like the panic Mary Alice feels when she has to stand up and recite in front of the class? I hear footsteps, the porch light comes on and then the door opens.

"Yes?" a man says. He's about Dad's age and size, but already nearly bald. His suit coat and tie are off and his shirt open at the collar. His expression is quizzical, but not threatening, so I start my pitch.

"Hello, Sir. I'm Alec Lewis from the *Oregon Journal*, and—"He holds up a hand to stop me. "And you'd like to sign me up for delivery, right? Sure, we took it up in Portland. I was wondering when you guys would come around. Can you start it tomorrow?"

Is it this easy? I'm so stunned I have trouble pulling out the order sheet. He takes it and fills it in himself, marking it for daily and Sunday and signing in the right place without any prompting. "Delivered the *Journal* myself back in the 30's," he explains. "Same old order form. Nothing's changed but the price."

"Th-thank you, Sir!" I manage to stammer. "This is my first try signing someone up."

"Really? Then let me give you a piece of advice. Have the order form in your hand and start your pitch as soon as they open the door—and always smile and look 'em right in the eye. Never look down or away." He wishes me goodnight and closes the door. The porch light goes out and I sprint back to the Chevy, waving the order form like a battle flag.

"Beginner's luck!" Ferraday growls. "Why can't I ever get someone like that?"

"Never mind, Joe," J. P. says. "We'll give you a couple more shots. Let's see if those folks out by the college are home yet."

They aren't, so we let Joe try a couple of the local move-ins. No luck. "That's okay," J. P. says as Ferraday trudges back from the second attempt. "I'll take you next week and you'll get one. We got two tonight, so let's go celebrate. How do shakes and fries for everyone sound?"

"Yeah, Man!" Rush exclaims, and even Ferraday brightens up.

We head out to Irv's, a hamburger joint on the south end of town out by the college. I've heard of it, but I've never been there before. "Triple order of fries—the big basket!" J. P. calls out as we take a booth in one corner.

"And shakes!" Rush adds. "Three of 'em. J. P.'s paying tonight."

"What kind?" Irv asks. "As if I didn't already know."

"Graveyard, Man! What else?"

"What's that?" I ask quickly. I'm partial to chocolate myself.

"Everything on the fountain," Ferraday explains. "Irv makes 'em just for us and the Linfield football team. Costs J. P. a nickel extra. You man enough to drink one?"

"Sure," I say, although I have second thoughts as I watch Irv take the container, scoop in the ice cream, add milk and then go right down the syrup line adding a squirt of everything—chocolate, strawberry, lemon-lime, cherry, grape, root beer and hot fudge. J. P. settles for a cup of coffee, and I'm thinking, *maybe I should have stuck with plain chocolate.*

"Don't worry," Rush tells me. "It tastes a lot better than it looks."

"Yeah, they're a little different each time," Ferraday adds. "Sorta depends on which knob Ol' Irv leans on the hardest."

By the time Irv finishes the shakes, the fries are done too. He brings them in a huge basket, plonks down three bottles of ketchup for us and we dig in. They're greasy and salty enough to make a dietitian cringe, but we don't give a rip. And the shakes do taste better than they look. J. P. gives Irv two dollars for everything and gets change back.

And we talk. Some of it is junior high stuff that goes over my head, but hey, I'm part of the group now. As we munch and guzzle, I suddenly realize that this is my gang, my family. There's been no initiation. I don't have a badge or a pin or a letter, but I'm a member now, a working guy, part of a brotherhood doing something important, with people counting on us every day.

The rift with my old Cozine teammates is patched up and forgotten, but we all realize that from now on they will be missing one average blocking back, so-so forward and mediocre third baseman. And the scout troop will be short one tenderfoot. A few years later I will read Robert Frost's *The Road Not Taken*, and the images of the roads splitting apart and the traveler choosing the one less traveled by and the difference it makes in his life will stay with me for the rest of my days. Does one little choice make such a difference? You bet it does!

****

On Tuesday Janet Tabor and I go to war. It begins outside at recess, with Larry Dale and me locked in a game of mumblestretch. I'm good enough to beat him any time I want, but he's a lot tougher than I am, so it's a good idea to let him win once in a while. I'm just deciding to let him win this one and then take him two out of three when Janet Tabor sneaks through the group of guys watching us, taps us both on the shoulder and calls, "Winners!"

I'm had and I know it. If we see Janet coming, we can end the game, straighten up and not have to accept her challenge. But if you're tapped while playing, you must accept. I look around, hoping one of the guys will claim he already has winners, but nobody does. Okay, I'll throw the game to Larry. But he thinks the same thing. He suddenly loses his balance (*yeah, sure*), sits down hard on the grass and says, "You win, Alec."

So I get slowly back up and try to look nonchalant. "Mumblestretch?" I ask hopefully. There at least I stand a chance. But the challenger gets to name the game, and Janet shakes her head.

"No. Straight stretch. Same as you were playing." She's already stretching and flexing her legs. She's wearing a flared skirt and petticoat, so she has full range of motion. Her legs are longer, she can do the full splits, and I can't. She's got me and we both know it.

In mumblestretch you have to match the throw of your opponent, and I know some really tricky ones that I'll bet Janet can't match. But in straight stretch it's just stick the knife in the ground any old way you choose, and Janet misses a simple stick about as often as Pee Wee Reese muffs a routine grounder.

I take my time, trying to prolong the game until recess is over, but Janet stretches out with me until I'm extended as far as I can go. Then, just to show off, she drops into the full splits and sticks her knife a foot beyond any point I could possibly reach. That really burns me. I can take losing, even to a girl, but casually doing the splits like that is rubbing it in a bit too much. So even as she beats me, I'm developing a nasty scheme for revenge. If my timing is right, it might just work.

Recess has to be over in less than a minute. None of the guys have tapped us and called winners. So, even as I concede, I tap her shoulder and call, "Rematch!"

"Sure," she says and then, thankfully, the buzzer goes off.

"Have to be some other time, I guess," I say as casually as I can.

"Anytime. Anyplace," she replies.

Thank you, Janet! You say just what I want to hear, and you say it in front of witnesses too.

****

Since Dad is an accountant, the first half of April is his busiest time of the year. To listen to him at the dinner table, you would think the whole world is coming to him with tax problems that have to be sorted out right now, this very minute. No wonder his mood goes sour on the first and stays that way until the seventeenth or eighteenth. I've learned to keep very quiet and stay out of his way until the tax-filing deadline passes.

But on Friday the seventeenth he finally comes home in a jaunty mood and announces that he is going back to school. "Whatever do you mean by that?" Mom asks, and I wonder too.

"Two nights a week, over in Salem," he replies. "It's a cram course for the c.p.a. exam. I've decided to take another shot at it. Care to know why?"

"I suppose you'll tell me whether I care to or not," Mom says.

"Bob Timmons is going to quit the company and set up on his own. He says he'll take me in as a partner if I can pass the exam." He pauses to explain to me. "I almost passed it the first time, but I got distracted. The war came along, and so did you, Alec. I've never really had a reason to try for it since, but this is an opportunity I can't pass up. *Timmons & Lewis, Certified Public Accountants."* He traces the name in the air with his finger. "Sounds pretty good, huh?"

"*Lewis & Timmons* would sound better," I suggest.

"Nope. I'll be the junior partner, but a junior partner will make a lot more than I'm getting now. It could mean a nicer car this fall, maybe a house up on The Hill someday. Hey! We might even take the kind of vacations the Pattersons do someday."

"You mean, fly to places far away?" Now I'm getting excited.

"Could be, Alec. But you'll have to do your part."

"What do you want me to do?"

"It's a tough exam, so help out your mother while I'm studying. Do your route well. But mainly, just stay out of trouble so I'm not distracted. Think you can do that?"

"Sure. That's easy," I tell him, and I mean it too. But sometimes things that seem easy don't turn out that way.

****

On Thursday the 30th we get our bills for the month's papers, and I owe the *Oregon Journal* $58.23. Jeez Lou*eeze*! That's more money than I've ever had at one time in my whole life. We're not supposed to start collecting before the first, but I approach Dad that night. I give him the receipt and he hands over $1.95 in change.

"Here's two quarters, five dimes and nineteen nickels," he says. "Those nickels are for *all* your daily and Sunday customers. Use them! I don't want you pulling Scott's trick." He hands me a blue moneybag with drawstrings at the top. "I picked this up at the bank for you. For heaven's sake, don't get careless with it! If you need more change, come and see me. Good luck, Son!"

So I spend Friday afternoon and Saturday collecting, and by Saturday night I'm within three dollars of breaking even.

I'm trying to figure how much I'll have left after paying off J. P. but Dad warns me, not to count the profits until the money is in my hand. "Things can happen," he warns. After I collect five more times Sunday afternoon, he drives me over to J. P.'s house, where I pay off the bill and walk out with nearly five dollars in my pocket. And there's still more to come!

The total mounts slowly through the first week in May. I get a few aw-gee-I-don't-have-it-now-can-you-come-back-tomorrow stories, and one guy in an apartment over the Third Street shops is never home—except to pick up his paper. But six of the daily and Sunday customers tell me to keep the nickel, and I finally end up with just over twenty dollars for my first month's work. Dad makes me put ten in the bank, but the rest is mine to spend as I choose. Ooooh Man!

I don't forget Janet Tabor either. My idea has developed into a plan, but the conditions have to be just right. Finally, during the second week in May, things fall into place. It's another day that begins with clouds and a promise of rain, but they clear away and we get to go outside for afternoon recess.

In 1953 girls must wear dresses or skirts to school every day—no exceptions. The bolder ones will slip a pair of shorts on under their skirts if they want to play on the bars outside or try cartwheels or headstands in the gym, but by fifth grade most of them consider themselves too old for such things. Today Janet wears a tight skirt, not thinking we might go outside where I can challenge her. As we march out onto the playground, I tap her and call the rematch.

She gives me an angry look and says, "Not today, Alec."

"Why not?" I ask innocently.

"I can't. I'm not…dressed for it."

"You look like you're dressed to me. What's wrong?"

"I can't stretch out in this skirt. Besides, I don't have my knife."

"We can both use mine. I don't mind. Of course, if you're afraid to take me on…"

"I'm not afraid! This just isn't the right time."

"You said any place, any time. Okay, I say here and now."

"That's right, Janet," Claudia Forester says with a smirk. "I heard you."

"Whose side are *you* on?" Janet snarls, and Claudia just grins.

"I heard you too," Larry Dale chimes in. "I was right there beside Alec when you said it." He turns to me and adds in a stage whisper that can be heard thirty feet away. "What can you expect, Alec? She's just a girl. They never have any guts."

Of course that pushes Janet over the line, and she has to accept the challenge. "Let me see your knife," she says as we walk out onto the field. She sticks it a couple of times and admits the balance is pretty good. Then we face each other. I tell her, "You go first," and the game starts.

She sticks the knife close and I only have to stretch out a foot to pick it up. I deliberately stick it just six inches farther, and she turns sideways to me and stretches out to it. Now she has a choice. Does she want to play it safe—or go for broke with an unfamiliar knife? She plays it safe and I stretch out to two feet.

My turn, and I put it in the ground just a couple inches farther. She reaches it, but she has to tug her skirt up a ways. Larry and John Folsom whistle, but I keep my face blank. This makes her even madder. She jerks the knife out of the ground, aims for a point beyond my reach—and misses.

Larry picks it up and hands it to me. I pivot and stick it eight inches behind her back foot. I've got her now and everyone knows it. If she's smart, she'll give up. But Larry mutters, "Just a girl. No guts." So Janet tugs her skirt higher and stretches back to it. She tries another desperation toss and misses again. Hey, even Pee Wee Reese has a bad day once in a while.

I could end it right there, but I want to draw it out and teach her a lesson. I make her pull her skirt higher and stretch another three inches. She sticks it close. I stretch out, pick it up and stick it three more inches beyond her toe. Janet is game and goes for it, but her skirt is now up so high that Claudia begins to chant, "I see London. I see France…"

Larry and John must be getting an eyeful, but I keep looking right at Janet's face. She's mad and she's frustrated, but I don't see any fear. She aims closer this time and sticks it. It hurts, but I stretch out to it. I can easily plonk it beyond her reach now, but I want to see how game she is. So I stick the knife just eight inches beyond her front foot. She can reach it, pick it up and beat me—but she'll have to put her underpants on full public view to do it.

She hesitates and I start whistling *S-i-g-n-a-l. Signal! What are you going to do, Janet? How badly do you want to win?*

Well, I won't find out because Mr. Jackson saunters over, pulls Tabor back up by the arm and says, "Give it up, Janet. You lost this one."

So I win the game and get my revenge, but for some reason the victory seems hollow. No-guts Tabor? I don't think so. Maybe what she does is foolish, but it also takes courage. I want her to know I admire that, so I say, "Good game, Janet," and hold out my hand. She pretends not to see it and turns away.

Maybe it would all still blow over, but Larry has to open his big mouth. As we troop back in after recess, he catches up to her and says, "Hey Janet. You look real good in blue." Tabor has a red skirt and yellow blouse, so everyone knows what he means. *Larry,* I silently wish, *please keep your big mouth shut!*

What I win is merely the first round. I'm smart, cunning and patient—but so is Janet.

****

On May 18th the *Journal* announces that our jets shoot down twelve MIGs in the skies over Korea. Captain Joe McConnell gets three of them, running his total to 16 and moving him past Captain Manuel Fernandez, who has 14 , in the race for ace of aces. Both men are then pulled out of combat. An Oregon man, Lt. Colonel George Ruddell, gets his fifth MIG and becomes the 31st jet ace of the war.

On May 20 a Polish fighter pilot defects and flies a brand-new MIG-15 to Norway.

But in among the war stories is an article about a second t.v. station for Portland. KOIN will have a stronger signal that viewers can pick up from fifty to sixty miles away, and Morrisonville is just under forty miles south of Portland. It could be on the air before the year is over, and we could actually get television without being way up on The Hill—if we can afford it. Man, I hope Dad passes that test!

I also reserve a section in my journal for the baseball standings. Sure, pro football and basketball exist in 1953, but they don't have near the following that baseball has. So how are the teams doing after the first five weeks?

No surprises in the American League. The Yankees are leading and starting to pull away. In the National, a bit of a surprise. Philadelphia leads the newly-transplanted Milwaukee Braves by one, with the Dodgers two back. In the Pacific Coast League, the Portland Beavers are stuck in fourth place and not likely to climb any higher, but Dad has promised to take me up to see a Sunday doubleheader as soon as school is out and he passes his exam.

On the 21st Janet springs her trap.

Claudia Forester catches me as we come in from afternoon recess and asks if I can stay a few minutes after school lets out. I ask her what for.

"We're gonna play poor little lovebird. You know how it's done?"

I've heard about it, but I've never actually seen it. The sixth-grade girls play it after school occasionally, although they're not supposed to. It's sometimes called kiss or show, and it's a kind of variation on truth or dare.

A group of girls selects a "victim" and pins her arms behind her. Then they call four or five boys over, including one whom they suspect has a crush on the girl they are holding. The boys are lined up and then one or more of the girls chant, "Poor little lovebird, trapped up in a tree. Will Billy come and rescue her?"

Billy answers (or is supposed to answer), "No! Not me!"

Whereupon the leader takes the hem of the lovebird's skirt and raises it a few inches. Then they chant, "Poor little lovebird, lonely as can be. Will Jimmy come and rescue her?"

And Jimmy answers, "No! Not me!"

Then the leader calls the next boy, raising the skirt a little higher as she does. Sixth-grade girls in 1953 wear dresses three or four inches below the knee, so this can go on for a bit. Finally they call the boy who is supposed to be sweet on the victim, and he "saves" the lovebird by kissing her on the cheek. Then the victim is released and all the girls chant, "Two little lovebirds, sitting in a tree. K-i-s-s-i-n-g! First comes love, then comes marriage. Here comes Sharon (or whoever) with a baby carriage!"

But there can be complications. If the victim is really pretty and popular, one of the boys called first may decide to rescue her. That can lead to a squabble between two or more rescuers, and Mr. Hunter and Mr. Jackson will be getting out the boxing gloves. Or none of the boys may decide to step forward. Then the leader lifts the lovebird's skirt and slip all the way up to her waist—revealing that the "victim" has been warned in advance and has put a pair of shorts on over her panties. Then all the girls, victim included, chant, "Cowards! Cowards! All the boys are cowards!"

Then why do boys take part? Because every once in a while the victim has not been warned or is so confident of her rescuer that she doesn't put on shorts. You never can tell because the lovebird always squirms and pleads—does everything but scream. So we're never sure if she's actually caught without the shorts or she's just being a good actress.

"Who's the lovebird?" I ask Claudia.

"Carole Smith," she answers.

"Okay, I'll come. But I'm not going to kiss her."

"You don't have to. We think John Folsom really likes her."

That settles that. I am *definitely* not going to kiss any girl that John or Larry may really like. Either of them could wipe up the playground with me. I also wonder a bit because our unofficial, unwritten rules say that only sixth-graders can play lovebird. Of course we will be sixth-graders in a couple of weeks, and the game can be fun if you're not directly involved. What the heck? Carole Smith means nothing to me.

So, as soon as school lets out, I make for the spot where the girls hold the game. It's in an alcove formed where the gym juts out from the main building, and it's screened from view on three sides. The teachers keep an eye on it during recess, but after school they're all either in their rooms or out in front helping load the busses. Janet and Claudia already have Carole's arms pinned behind her back by the time I get there. Three other girls stand behind them. I'm surprised to see that one is Mary Alice.

Larry Dale joins me, but there is no sign of Folsom. "Where's John?" Janet asks, and Larry and I shake our heads.

"Didn't you tell him to come?" Claudia asks me.

"No. I thought you were telling everyone."

A wicked smile spreads across Tabor's face. "Well," she says. "If John isn't here, I guess we'll just have to pick another victim." She and Claudia release Carole, and the three of them suddenly grab Mary Alice. "Gee, only two boys here," Janet tells her. "Do you think one of them might come to your rescue? Let's see."

She pauses for effect and then begins to chant, "Poor little lovebird, trapped up in a tree. Will Larry come and rescue her?"

Larry apparently knows the game. He folds his arms and answers, "No. Not me."

"Gee, too bad!" Janet says as she grabs Mary Alice's skirt and pulls it up above her knees. "I guess we'll have to try again."

Okay, I see the trick. I'm going to have to step forward and kiss Mary Alice in front of Larry and the girls. It will be a little embarrassing, but what the heck? It's not like I haven't kissed her before. I wait for Tabor to call on me, but Janet has a better idea.

"Poor little lovebird, dress above her knee," she chants. "Won't Larry come and rescue her?"

Larry looks surprised, but again answers, "No. Not me."

"Tooo bad!" the girls chant, and Janet raises Mary Alice's skirt a few inches higher. Mary Alice has been standing in a kind of daze. Now she begins to squirm and struggle, but she's still the smallest girl in the class and no match for any of the five girls around her.

I wait for Janet to call my name, but of course she won't. How does she know that Mary Alice is my weak point? Well, it's probably not hard to figure out. Since school is almost out and she's moving to Denver in a couple of weeks, we get a bit careless. We don't hold hands in public or do anything that would get us into trouble at school, but the whole class can probably tell by the way we smile at each other or exchange a quick word that we're a twosome.

Meanwhile Janet continues to chant, "Poor little lovebird, lonely as can be. Won't Larry come and rescue her?"

"Hey!" Larry says. "Call on Alec. I said no."

"You say no? Tooo bad!" And Janet raises Mary Alice's skirt even higher.

Suddenly I see the rest of Janet's plan. She is not going to call on me. She will keep calling Larry's name until he agrees to kiss Mary Alice or I shove him out of the way. Either way, I get myself in a fight where I'll get my rear end kicked. "Okay Janet," I tell her. "You win. Call on me. I'll do it."

"Nope. I want to see Larry do it. What about it, Larry? Kiss or show?"

Larry Dale is a little slow at putting two and two together, but he finally begins to catch on. "She's Alec's girlfriend," he says. "Call on him." Janet shakes her head and Larry doubles a fist.

"Call on him, Tabor, or I'll rearrange your nose!"

Janet hesitates. She's probably a match for me, but Larry Dale is another matter. Once he gets mad, he would belt a girl and never mind the consequences. Meanwhile, Mary Alice stops squirming and starts to cry. She's a very modest girl who goes red with embarrassment if even her slip shows. But if Janet raises that skirt any higher, she'll be showing her panties as well.

"Come on Janet," says Claudia, who seems to change sides every five minutes. "Call on Alec. I want to see him smooch her."

Janet shrugs and gives in. "Poor little lovebird, lonely as can be," she chants. "Will Alec come and rescue her?"

"Yes!" I step forward and give Mary Alice a smack on the cheek, but Janet isn't satisfied.

"That's not good enough," she says.

"Whattya mean, not good enough?" I say as I step back. "I kissed her, didn't I?"

Janet winks at Claudia, who winks back. "That's not a real kiss. Give her a smooch right on the lips, or else..." She lifts the skirt even higher. Mary Alice wears pink underpants trimmed with white lace. Larry and I both look away, although he takes a couple of seconds longer to do it. I can't really blame him. If it were any girl other than Mary Alice, I'd be looking too.

Janet lowers Mary Alice's skirt just enough to cover her panties and says, "What about it, Alec? More of a kiss or more of a show?" So I step up and kiss Mary Alice right on the lips. She doesn't turn away from it, but her face seems frozen. It's almost like kissing a statue.

"Satisfied?" I ask Janet. She nods to the other girls and they release Mary Alice, but not before Janet flips her skirt and slip up past her waist before letting them drop.

Mary Alice runs sobbing for her bike, while Janet holds out her hand to me and says, mockingly, "Good game, Alec." I pretend not to notice it and turn away. Should I run after Mary Alice? What could I say if I catch up to her? I might let Janet have the last laugh, but she has to shoot off her big mouth again.

"Hey, you two!" she calls. "Tell Miss Peepants she looks really cute in pink!"

That does it! I spin around and start for Janet. Consequences or no consequences, licking or no licking, I'm going to bloody Tabor's nose but good! But Larry Dale grabs me and pulls me back. "Not here! Not now!" he growls. "That's what she wants. You'd have all five of 'em on ya. Wait! We'll get even later. I'll help ya."

Well, whatever I do will have to be done soon. The school year is over on Friday the 5th. That gives me just two weeks to come up with a plan and carry it out. Janet is being cautious too. She keeps her friends around her at recess and scoots straight for home as soon as school is out.

I reject half a dozen schemes before coming up with one that just might work. It's nasty, it's risky and it could sure land me in trouble. But Janet has hurt Mary Alice, just as surely as if she kicks or punches her, and I am going to make her pay for it, no matter what happens to me.

I catch up with Mary Alice at the library the next day and ask her, "What were you doing out there in the first place?"

"It was all Janet's idea," she tells me. "She'd been real nice to me for a week or so. She even invited me over to her place, and Mom let her come up to out house to have cookies and watch television. They don't have one." She starts to sniffle and her eyes tear up again. "She told me it would just be a little game to see if John would kiss Carole, and that she had her shorts on anyway if he wouldn't. Why was she so mean to me, Alec?"

"Because she wanted to hurt me."

"And all that being nice and wanting to be friends was?"

"A lie. She hurt you to hurt me, and I'm going to get even. Do you want to help?"

Mary Alice looks at me for a long time. Her sad, liquid eyes slowly grow clear and hard, like pond water about to freeze. "Yes," she says and turns away.

****

I start collecting again on the June first, and on the second the *Journal* carries two banner headlines. Elizabeth II is formally crowned Queen of Great Britain, and Edmund Hillary, a New Zealander, becomes the first man to make it to the top of Mount Everest. On the third the atomic spies, Julius and Ethel Rosenberg, spurn the government's last "talk or die" offer and their execution date is set for the eighteenth.

On the fourth, it looks like a truce in Korea may finally happen, and we also test an atomic bomb in Nevada. The blast is powerful enough to be felt in parts of Oregon.

On the fifth, the very last day of school, Janet Tabor finally drops her guard.

We have Monday of the week off for Memorial Day, go a full day Tuesday and Wednesday, half a day Thursday and come in for one hour Friday afternoon to pick up our report cards, have a little party and say goodbye for the summer. I've just about given up any hope of getting back at Janet at school. But just as we get ready to leave, Mrs. Foster asks if anyone could stay for a few minutes to help her clean up. Amazingly, Tabor's hand goes up. So does mine.

Maybe Janet feels safe knowing Mrs. Foster is in the room. Maybe she just wants to show she's not afraid of me. Whatever the reason, I catch Mary Alice's eye, then Larry's and give them a nod. They both nod back.

Janet and I work silently together for a few minutes, piling party leftovers into a large wastebasket., while the rest of the class leaves. Then Mary Alice slips back in, goes to the far side of Mrs. Foster's desk and begins talking with her. By this time Tabor and I have the wastebasket full. Our last job is to haul it down to the janitor's closet.

"Want me to carry it Janet?" I ask. "It looks kind of heavy."

"For you, maybe," she sneers. I've already untied my right shoe. Now, as she picks up the wastebasket, I pretend to notice it.

"Sheesh!" I mutter as I drop to one knee to tie it.

"Clumsy!" she remarks as she starts to edge around me with the wastebasket. Mrs. Foster, talking with Mary Alice, has her back to us. Perfect!

As Janet shifts her weight to her front leg, my right arm snakes out, hooks around that leg just above the ankle, and I yank up and back as hard as I can. The wastebasket goes flying as Janet instinctively throws out her arms to protect herself. For an instant Janet Tabor is parallel to the floor and not quite three feet above it. It's a very hard and unforgiving floor, linoleum over concrete. Janet lands full length with a very satisfying *whomp!*

But she doesn't get up.

Chapter Ten: Tin Cans

S*weet Lord Jesus, Alec! What have you done this time?*
No, I'm not cussing. That's my Presbyterian conscience arriving, as usual, a couple of seconds too late to stop me from doing something absolutely stupid, but in plenty of time to make me feel good and guilty about it. Why do I always see the consequences so clearly once they get here, but never when they are on the way and might be headed off?

Janet lies flat on her stomach, not even moving a finger, while Mrs. Foster comes out of her chair like a sprinter leaving the starting blocks. I holler, "God, Janet! Are you okay?" and I mean every word of it. Mary Alice gives a little gasp and Larry appears, as planned, in the doorway.

Mrs. Foster kneels beside Janet and gently turns her over. There's no blood, no sign of anything broken. Then she blinks rapidly, makes some odd little gasping sounds, and I realize she just has the wind knocked out of her. It happens to me once in football. A Fox Glen lineman catches me off guard and buries his helmet in the pit of my gut. When that happens, you're totally helpless. All you can do is lie there and wait for things to shift back into place.

"What happened?" Mrs. Foster asks me. Her voice is concerned, but not angry—as if she were silently adding, *I know a boy like you wouldn't do something this terrible deliberately.* That doesn't make me feel any better.

"She—she must have tripped over me," I lie. "I was tying my shoe and…"

"Yeah!" Larry chimes in right on cue. "Alec was tying his shoe. She musta tripped over his foot."

Somehow it doesn't sound convincing. Not to me and not to Mrs. Foster, who is no dummy. So she turns to Mary Alice and asks her, "Did you see what happened?"

Mary Alice looks doubtful for a moment, until she hears Janet's breathing start to come back. Then she squats down beside Mrs. Foster, looks Janet right in the eye and says, "She tripped over Alec's foot. It was all just an accident."

Mrs. Foster gives us all her best *there's-more-to-this-than-meets-the-eye* look, but apparently decides to let the matter drop, and I feel like a fighter saved by the bell in the last round. "Larry, help Alec pick up the trash and take it down to the janitor's closet," Mrs. Foster orders. "Mary Alice, help me get Janet back up—no, wait! Let's let her get her breath back first. That was a very nasty spill, Janet. You might have been seriously hurt. I hope you will all learn to be more careful."

Is it my imagination or does her last sentence carry more than one meaning?

By the time Larry and I get the garbage picked up and lugged down to the janitor's closet, Janet is her belligerent old self once more. "You lied!" she says as she confronts us in the hall. "You all lied! Alec, you tripped me deliberately and lied to the teacher about it! Well, God saw it too! Remember that!"

That really irks me. Why does Janet have to drag God into our own private feud? Well, two can play that game.

"You're right, Janet," I tell her. "I feel really bad about it too. Would you like me to go back in there and confess?"

"You wouldn't dare!" she sneers.

"Oh yes I would! I'll march right in there and tell Mrs. Foster exactly what happened. But only on one condition."

"What's that?"

"You have to come in with me and confess what you did to Mary Alice, and you have to go first—*and* Mary Alice will be right there with us to fill in anything you leave out."

Janet considers the possibilities and for a moment I'm afraid she's going to call my bluff. "She'll make two phone calls," I add quickly. "I know what will happen to me. I'll get a big lecture and maybe be grounded for a few days. What will your dad do?"

Apparently he would do plenty, because Janet gives me one last dirty look and says, "Okay, we'll settle this in the fall." And I know she means it.

So I win another round, but my conscience won't let me enjoy it. I close my eyes and see images of Janet with a broken nose, broken teeth or her head split open. If she doesn't have the reflexes of a cat, it might turn out that way. Then I *would* be in deep, deep do-do. I hope Mary Alice appreciates the risk I took for her.

She doesn't. I see her at the library later that afternoon. It's her last day, so Mrs. Carruthers lets her walk down to the swing with me. Again we sit facing each other and pump with our feet to get it going. Finally I ask her, "Do you really feel bad about what I did to Janet?"

"Yes," she says.

"It was wrong, I guess. But I did it for you."

"But why did you have to do that?"

"Well, what did you expect?"

She thinks about it for a couple of swings. "I hoped you and Larry might pull her into the closet and hold her arms. Then I could do what she did to me."

"You'd try that on Janet? She'd whale the daylights out of you."

"How could she? We're leaving for Denver on Sunday."

I guess I deliberately block out the fact that she's leaving, because all of a sudden it's there right in front of me. Mary Alice will be out of my life, perhaps forever, in two more days. I swallow hard and ask her, "Are you going to miss this place?"

"Some of it, I guess. Not the school. I never really fit in. It'll be nice to start over and make some new friends. But I will miss—well, a few people."

"I hope I'm one of them."

"You're at the top of the list."

She slides over on her seat, just a few inches, but her meaning is obvious even to someone as dense as I am. *Come over and sit beside me.* I feel awkward, eager, smooth and clumsy all at once. Do I take her hand? Put an arm around her? Kiss her? All three at once? Well, I start by holding her hand.

"I'll miss you too. Lots."

She snuggles against me, and I slip an arm around her shoulder. I'm about to try kissing her when we hear yells and see a bunch of little kids heading our way on bicycles. We slip out of the swing and walk away from the play area to the edge of the hill leading down to the bottom of the park. We can see the footbridge across the little creek and beyond it the hill sloping up again and its covering of dense trees and shrubs.

I take her hand and start down the hill, but she holds back. "No, Alec," she says. "I'm not ready for that. Not yet. You aren't either. But I promise I'll come back someday, when we're older. And then..." She looks around to make sure the kids on the bicycles are gone. Then she kisses me once, very softly, and says, "Let's go back to the library. I don't want to look at this place anymore. It's too sad."

We walk back together and, ten minutes later, she's in her dad's new Cadillac and waving goodbye to me as it glides off down Adams Street. I'm glad we didn't go down across the creek because she's right—we're not ready for that yet. But as I wave back, I suddenly realize that I may never see her again.

****

Mom and Dad always make a big production out of examining my report card. Well, it's a good one this time. I get all A's except for a C in penmanship, and Mrs. Foster adds a great little note in the section reserved for comments. *It has been a pleasure watching Alec mature into a fine young gentleman. His reading and writing skills especially have shown tremendous improvement. He may well have a future as a writer or journalist.*

Of course she writes this before I nearly cripple Janet right under her nose. I should be happy with a report this good, but I feel almost as bad as if I get the A's by cheating.

Dad, like Mrs. Foster, is no dummy. He can read my mood easily enough, but he knows that confronting me will only make me clam up. He waits until bedtime, then comes up and raps once on my door. I'm lying on my bed holding the Nieuport 17 that Mary Alice has given back because she can't take it with her to Denver. Her dad tells her it's best to cut all links with Morrisonville and not worry because there are plenty of boys in Colorado.

"Something bothering you, Alec?" Dad asks after I tell him to come in.

"Not really."

"Then do you want to tell me about it?"

I want to tell somebody, but not Dad. His exam is just a few days away, and I can't distract him from it. Pietrowski is a Catholic, and I remember him telling me about going to confession a couple of times a year, telling the priest about everything he's done wrong and then being officially forgiven. I don't think my church does that. I wonder, would the priest at St. James allow a Presbyterian to confess to him?

"Dad, I'm not in any trouble," I say. "It's just that..."

He looks at the Nieuport in my hands and guesses. "Mary Alice had to give it back, huh? Your first girlfriend, and now you have to say goodbye."

"That's—part of it."

Dad jangles his keys as he thinks. "Tell you what," he finally says. "You need a little break, if only for just a day. Why don't we take you over to see your grandpa and grandma on Sunday? You haven't had a good visit with them since Christmas. I could take you over right after church. You could spend the night and then come home in time to do your route on Monday."

"That would be great!" Hey, if Grandpa Fullerton isn't the world's greatest listener and problem-solver, then he's right up there with the leaders. He's wonderful at explaining, since he can get me to see the point of something without making me feel like an idiot for missing it in the first place.

So I do my route Sunday morning, come home for breakfast and a change of clothes and we all go to church. Then I change again and Dad drives me to Hopewell, a tiny community about halfway between Morrisonville and Salem. By the time we get there, Grandpa Fullerton's old Studebaker is waiting at the Hopewell General Store. I toss my overnight bag in the back seat, pile in beside him and we head for Salem.

It's a quiet ride because Grandpa rarely talks while he drives, concentrating on the road ahead as if desperadoes are lurking in ambush. He's a small, wiry man who still has a full head of hair as white as Santa's beard, but there's still some brown in his carefully-clipped mustache. I remember asking him once why this is so.

"Well," he explains, "my hair is sixty-seven years old now, but my mustache is only about forty-five."

Grandma Fullerton is plump, the way grandmothers are supposed to be. Her hair is iron-gray and, like Mrs. Carruthers, she smells faintly of lavender. She's also certain that I don't get enough to eat, so she has a huge dinner of meat loaf and mashed potatoes waiting. Normally I don't like meat loaf, but hers is okay. After I finish, she asks if I want some cake and ice cream, but Grandpa shakes his head.

"Not now," he says. "We'll save that for just before bedtime. Tell you what, Alec. Let's us do the washing up while Grandma makes us a bunch of popcorn. Then what say we go down and see how the trains are doing?"

I know for sure now that Dad has told Grandpa I have something I need to get off my chest. Grandpa is a retired conductor for the Southern Pacific and, as I've said, one of the world's best listeners. It probably comes from thirty years of dealing with passengers. Put Grandpa next to a set of tracks and his whole face changes. Let a steam locomotive come chuffing by and his eyes seem glow like headlights in a fog.

He counts the other cars as we pull into the lot by the Southern Pacific Depot and then shakes his head disapprovingly. "Just a handful now," he says. "Used to be dozens, practically any time of the day."

"Maybe more will come," I say.

He gives me a smile and pats my shoulder. "Always the optimist, huh? Well, we'll see." He takes a conductor's watch from his vest and checks the time. Since it's Sunday, he wears the blue serge suit and vest of a Southern Pacific conductor. "Shasta Daylight's due in about an hour. The milk train from Portland should be in before then, and there'll probably be a freighter or two." He always calls them *freighters* and not *freights*—as if that somehow gives them a personality and identity.

Grandma provides us with a big tub of popcorn, which we set on the seat between us. She doesn't salt it because Grandpa has to watch his blood pressure, but she melts half a stick of oleomargarine over it. Grandpa takes a piece or two at a time, while I stuff it in my mouth by the fistful. "Don't see where you make room for it, Alec," he comments as I chew like a cow with a cud.

I take that as a subtle hint to slow down, so I scan the block signals to the north and south of the station. No lights on either one, but a tinny rattle from across the tracks catches my attention. There's a cannery set just on the other side of a spur track running parallel to the main line. It's a long, low building with slab sides painted dark green and silver and a corrugated iron roof.

I know it's too early for beans, but the cannery is up and running nevertheless. The rattle comes from a stream of shiny empty cans that pop out of an opening in the wall to the north of where we park, then rattle their way south for twenty or thirty feet along a conveyor belt before disappearing back through another opening. As they move they jiggle and rattle as though they are alive. Periodically the belt stops and the cans sit motionless. Then the belt starts again and the jiggling, rattling march continues. The effect is somehow hypnotic. I watch the marching cans while Grandpa watches me watching them.

"You know, Alec?" he says at last. "Shakespeare said that all the world's a stage and that all men and women are players on it. Did you ever think that life might be a conveyor belt, and we're all just tin cans moving along it?

"What do you mean?"

"Well, we make our appearance, rattle our way along the line and then disappear through another door. And after a while, no one can remember that we were even here."

I don't know what to make of that. Grandpa is is trying to get me to see something, but what? I take a stab at it and say, "We have to be more than a bunch of cans, Grandpa. We have souls."

"Tell me, Alec. What are souls good for?"

"Well…" I try hard to remember some phrases we learn in Sunday School. The best I can come up with is, "They remind us that we're the children of God."

"And what do we do if we're the children of God?"

That one I do remember. "Love God and each other."

"And what happens when we don't?" he asks as he nibbles more popcorn.

Before I can frame an answer, I see an amber light come on. "North board's gone yellow, Grandpa."

He checks his watch again. "Too early for the milk train. It's either a freighter or a switch engine. Wait for the whistle and see if you can tell."

We wait a few minutes and the signal goes red. Then I hear the first whistle up at Market Street, about a mile away. A long, lonesome *Huh-woot!* Steam engine. How fast is it coming? I wait for the second whistle, a quarter mile closer. *Huh-woot!* "A freighter," I announce. "Big one. Coming pretty fast."

"Correct," Grandpa says. "A Baldwin four-six-two, I'll bet."

I know better than to bet against Grandpa when it comes to trains. We listen as the whistle becomes louder and more frequent. Then the warning bells and lights at the Mill Street crossing at the north end of the lot activate. With a last long *Huh-wooot!* And a flash of its headlight, the engine swings around a corner and we get out of the car to watch it roar past. Grandpa waves to the engineer—he probably knows him—while I count the wheels on the old Baldwin engine. Four guide wheels, six big drivers and two stabilizers behind them. Grandpa is right again.

As soon as the engine and tender go past, I start counting the cars. Forty-four, counting the crummie, which is what Grandpa calls the caboose. About halfway along I see a man stick his head out the door of an empty boxcar and wave at us.

"Grandpa, did you see the hobo?" I ask.

"Yep," he says. "Just a youngster with no brains. He should never show himself while he's passing through a station. Stationmaster could spot him and call on ahead, and he'd have the railroad police waiting for him next time she stops."

"Would they really do that?"

"Most wouldn't bother, but there's a few that are mean enough. And even the nice ones could be having a bad day, and that just might push 'em into doing it. Sometimes folks are born mean, and sometimes they grow that way over time, and sometimes—well, they just think they can get away with it, so why not?"

"Grandpa?" I ask. "Can I tell you something?"

The old man carefully selects two pieces of popcorn and inspects them as if there is some hidden meaning in their shape. "That's why we came down here," he says as he finally pops them in his mouth.

So I tell him about my war with Janet—how it smolders since we start at Cozine five years ago and then breaks out this spring—right up to the point where I spill her on the floor. By the time I finish the north board is yellow again.

"That'll be the milk train," he says. "Let's watch it come in, and then we'll have a talk."

We watch the board go red, and then we hear the whistle—the *Huh-woot!* of another steam engine. They sound pretty much alike to me, but Grandpa says, "That'll be 718. Ridden it many's the time."

The train swings around the corner, pulls into the station and stops. We get out of the car and stroll over by the engine. I check the number on the tender—718. Grandpa climbs the three-rung steel ladder at the back of the cab and speaks briefly with the engineer. Then he climbs back down and the engineer beckons to me. "His name is Mr. Davis," Grandpa says. "Go ahead, but just for a second."

Nervously, I mount the ladder. I've never been in an engine cab before, and I'm trying to look everywhere at once, trying to think of what to ask, trying to fix everything in my memory forever. But it's all a jumble. Mr. Davis points to things, tells me their names and what they're for—for some reason the Johnson Bar is what sticks in my mind—while the fireman leans on his shovel and grins at me. I remember the vibration under my feet, as if the engine is a living, breathing creature—an athlete catching its breath and eager to be off again. Then the engineer points to Grandpa waving at me to come back, so I scramble down the ladder as the conductor shouts, "Boooard!"

When the train leaves, I look once more at the cans jiggling their way along the conveyer line like little tin soldiers marching out of step. "I was pretty stupid, wasn't I? I could have really hurt her bad."

"No," Grandpa says. "You weren't stupid. You were foolish."

"Same thing, isn't it?"

"Not at all," he tells me. "If you're stupid, you lack brains. If you're foolish, what you lack is experience. Look, Alec. I think it was Mark Twain who said that any boy who attempts to carry an old tomcat home by picking it up by the tail is going to learn more in two seconds about how not to carry a cat than he would in two hours of classroom instruction. Now you might try carrying the cat that way once. That would be foolishness. Would you try it twice?"

"Not on your life!"

"Then you're not stupid."

"But I shouldn't have done it at all! Why didn't I see what might happen?"

"I suppose it's because we just don't think sometimes. We lash out without realizing what we're doing. Do you know I once did something like that, only worse? I almost killed a man once—deliberately—and I was quite a bit older than you are now, so I should have known better."

"*You* almost killed someone?" Hey, this is my sweet old grandpa talking! I can't remember him even raising his voice more than once or twice. "Was it in the war?"

"Nope. I was too young for the Spanish-American War and just too old for World War I. Happened when I was working for the Erie Railroad back in Ohio around 1905.

There was a strike on, and I was one of the guards protecting the line. I could just as easily have been one of the strikers, but no—I was on management's side that time. We carried clubs, but the bosses said no guns. They didn't want anyone killed. It would have been bad publicity.

"Anyhow, I was patrolling the yards when I came across two strikers trying to tamper with a switch. They were what we called Shanty Irish back then. We looked on 'em about the same way that whites down in Mississippi look on Negroes today. I yelled and went for 'em with my club. After all, they could have caused a wreck! I didn't plan to do any more than run 'em off, but one of 'em was drunk and he showed fight."

"What did he do, Grandpa?"

"He pulled a knife and took a swipe at me. I was lucky he was too drunk to have any coordination. 'Course, if he'd been sober, he wouldn't have tried a dang-fool thing like that. Well, he overbalanced and staggered on past me a few steps, and that gave me a clear shot at him.

"Now, I could have kicked him good and hard or maybe given him a rap on the back of his head. Either one would have put him down and taken all the starch out of him. But no—I was mad! That dang drunk had just tried to gut me like a fish!"

Grandpa gives a long sigh, looks at the popcorn and decides not to take any. I wait for him to continue and try to picture my dear old grandpa fighting for his life.

"I let him recover and come for me again. Then I swung that club like I was Babe Ruth going for the fences—and I got him right on the side of his head! I still remember the shock that went up my arm, and I swear I could feel his skull give way. Anyhow, he just folded up like an empty gunny sack.

"His friend just stared at me and cried, 'Jayzus! Yuv killed 'im!' But my blood was up and I told him, 'You get him on outa here and don't come back or I'll do the same for you!' And I meant it too. It was like this cold rage had just taken over my body, and I was ready to do anything."

"But the man didn't die, did he, Grandpa?"

"No. He lived. Don't ask me how. But from what I heard, he was never quite right in the head after that. I must have scrambled his brains good and proper."

"Did they arrest you for it?"

"Nope. You see, I was an Erie Railroad employee protecting Erie Railroad property, and the Erie Railroad pretty much ran the county back then. But I had made myself a little too hot to handle. Some of that Irishman's friends were looking to kill me, and there was a good chance they would have. So the railroad had me change my name and sent me out west with a letter of recommendation to the Southern Pacific. And that's how I wound up in Oregon and met your grandma."

"You mean that Fullerton isn't really your name?" This really jolts me.

"It is now, but it's not the one I was born with. That part of me died the day I slugged that Irishman—never did learn what his name was. I'd like to think that the rage died with it, and that Charles Fullerton is a better man than the one who swung that club. That's the point, Alec. You can learn from what you do. You can pick the cat up a different way. You don't have to swing the club a second time."

"Someday will you tell me what your name used to be?"

"No, I'd rather not. That man doesn't exist anymore. And I want you to promise not to tell Grandma or your mother or anyone else about it. Not until I'm dead and gone and you're all grown. Then, if you decide to be a writer, you can look it up. In the meantime, what are you going to do about this Tabor girl?"

"I don't know, Grandpa. What *can* I do?"

"You owe her a rematch, that much is sure. I think you ought to go right up to her, first day back, and offer to play her, fair and square, and let her pick the time and place."

"She'll beat me, Grandpa."

"How do you know that?"

"Well, she's a little taller than I am. Plus she can do the splits."

"And you can't?"

"No. None of the boys can."

"Then why don't you become the first? You've got almost three months to practice."

It's an interesting idea, but I have my doubts. "Do you really think I could do it?"

"Alec, what I think is beside the point. Do *you* think you could do it?"

It's a challenge thrown at me, and I know only one way to respond. "Yes, I think I could." Then the doubts return. "But she'd still probably beat me."

"Are you afraid of losing, Alec? No one goes through life undefeated."

"Yeah, but she's a girl!"

"Exactly! Just put yourself in her shoes for a minute. She's strong, she's athletic, but what can she do? Can she play on the football team? Or the basketball or baseball teams? I know they won't let her wrestle or box. Could she even deliver papers like you do?"

"No. Girls aren't allowed. Only boys."

"So, how do those shoes feel on you?"

"Pretty cramped," I admit.

"Then give her a shot at you. She could wind up as a good friend."

"I don't think so. She probably hates me after all we've done. Grandpa, don't tell anyone I said this, but I'm kinda scared of her."

"I don't think you need to be afraid of this Tabor girl. There's another one I'd worry about, if I were you."

"Who, Grandpa?"

"The one who seems to stay in the background and egg everyone on. I think you said her name was Forester."

"Claudia? You think she could be behind all this?"

"I wouldn't be surprised. I've known people like that. They won't dirty their own hands, but they love to see others mix it up. They're like the puppet masters pulling the strings behind the curtain. Tabor doesn't sound like the kind of girl who'd be that sneaky. She might come right out and pop you on the nose, but I don't think she'd plan anything like that game by herself. I think Forester is using the both of you."

"You think we're both being played for suckers?" I close my eyes and I can see Claudia, never in the forefront, but always just a row or two away, smiling innocently while others do the dirty work.

"Yes, I'd say you both picked that old cat up right by the tail. The point is, are you going to learn anything from it?"

"I will, but I don't know about Janet."

"She will if you explain, but you can't do that until you play her. So I suggest you start practicing tonight. Look! Here comes a switch engine to fill up."

One of the little pufferbellies, as Grandpa calls them, makes its way up the spur track to a water tower set between the spur and main line and almost directly across from where we're parked. "Watch him, Alec," Grandpa says. "I want you to remember this."

So I watch the fireman jump off the engine, climb a ladder up the tower, grab a pole with a hook on the end and use it to swing the spout around until it's right over the boiler. He already has the boiler lid open. Next, he turns a big iron wheel until water pours from the spout and into the boiler. Then, after it's full, he turns the handle until the flow stops, closes the lid, swings the spout away from the engine, climbs down and the engine backs away. The whole operation takes maybe a couple of minutes.

"Why do you want me to remember that?" I ask.

"Because the days of steam are almost over. If you ever come back here with your grandson, there won't be any water towers. There won't be any steam engines either. It will all be diesel in just a few years, but you can tell your grandkids how you watched them fill the boilers."

I think about that as I munch popcorn and watch the tin cans jiggle along the conveyor. Then I hear the *woonk* of a diesel horn and notice that the north block light has gone green.

"That'll be the Shasta Daylight," Grandpa says, and of course he's right.

It roars into the station like a huge orange and gold serpent with one enormous yellow eye. Porters jump down a second or two before it comes to a full stop, place their stools and unload passengers as others line up to get on. It's all done in a controlled hurry, as if it's somehow demeaning to stop such an important train in such a little station. From my seat beside Grandpa I watch the embraces as people say hello and goodbye.

Then the baggage cart pulls away. Porters grab their footstools and climb back on board as the conductor waves to the engineer and the horn gives two short warning blasts. Then the Daylight shudders into motion. With studied nonchalance the conductor grabs a handhold as an open doorway glides past, swings himself on board, and the orange and gold serpent vanishes around the north bend as the board goes red. I hear the *woonk!*—I never can think of that noise as a whistle—at the crossings, fainter and fainter as it gathers speed and rushes north.

One by one the cars leave the station until we are the only ones left, and there's nothing to watch except the tin cans jiggling their way along the conveyer line.

"Might as well head back," Grandpa says as he fires up the Studebaker. "Grandma's going to be wondering what happened to us."

Chapter Eleven: Shadows Cast

C*oming events cast their shadows before them.*

As a schoolgirl back in the 1890's, Grandma Fullerton wins a penmanship medal by writing that sentence three times in one minute and doing it more neatly than any other pupil in the county. It becomes her favorite saying, and she teaches it to me as soon as I am old enough to remember and repeat. I learn it very early, but I can never write it (or anything else) in a hand that even comes close to Grandma's beautiful copperplate script. I think she would be even more pleased with me if I receive an A in penmanship and C's in everything else.

But I am to remember that saying and the meaning behind it as the days lengthen and the shadows of summer stretch out before me…

****

Yes, summer finally comes to Western Oregon. The rains stop, the clouds dissolve like snow under a warm sun and the temperature climbs through the seventies and finally nudges at eighty. There are golden days for me after school is out, but Saturdays have to be the best. Let me take you through one and show you why.

It's the morning of Saturday, June 20, and there's no schedule because it's Mom's day to sleep in. Breakfast this one day is on a fix-it-yourself-when-you-want basis. Dad has set out cereal, juice, milk, butter and bread for toasting. The only rule is that everyone cleans up after himself.

Dad is already up, finished with his breakfast and having a quiet pipe while he reads the editorial page of *The Oregonian* before going to work. (He puts in half a day on Saturdays.) I'm still in pajamas when I pour a glass of orange juice, fix a bowl of Kellog's Krumbles and grab the funnies to see how Dick Tracy and Li'l Abner are doing. I'm loyal to the *Journal*, but I have to admit *The Oregonian* carries good comics.

Dad puts down his section long enough to tell me that the Portland Beavers will be at home a week from Sunday for a doubleheader against Los Angeles. "Think you might want to go up and see it?" he asks. I just grin and he knows the answer to that one. Dad has finished up his exam this week, and he's certain that he's nailed it. I sure hope he's right.

After Dad leaves for work at eight o'clock, I turn our old Philco to KEX for *No School Today*. (I'm a little ashamed to admit that I still like the adventures of Big Jon and Sparkie the Elf. After all, I *am* eleven now.) When the program ends, I clean up my breakfast dishes, go up and get dressed and at 9:30 listen to *Space Patrol*, which, along with *The Lone Ranger*, is my favorite kids' program. (*The Whistler*, my absolute favorite, is supposed to be for grownups.)

Mom puts in an appearance and asks if I'll be going to the movies this afternoon. I tell her yes and she says she'll have lunch ready for me at noon, so I am not to fill up on junk beforehand. Then she pours me a cup of coffee, well-sweetened with sugar and cream, and at 10:30 I'm heading for Benny's.

The papers arrive about 10:45 and by eleven I'm out on the route. I've picked up one new customer, so I'm now carrying 41 dailies, a bulldog for Mr. Lofgren and a yesterday edition in case I run into Cap'n Andy. I'm in a hurry to finish, but I still have to stop for a quick word with Mom Jenkins, Frank at the barber shop and the cop behind the desk at the police station. It's not Officer D this morning. I guess he's out on patrol or off duty.

After I get the apartments, I double back for Stannard's and the Blue Moon. Hey! Bet I'm the only 11-year-old in town who can walk into a saloon by himself and say hi to the bartender. Of course, I have to scoot as soon as I give him the paper.

Mrs. Carruthers has talked me into working two mornings a week at the library, helping her sort and shelve books. I agree to it because I want an argument to use with Dad if he asks me to pick berries or beans a couple of days a week. (*Look, Dad. I'm already doing something important and useful.*) Well, that's my motive at first, but now I actually find it interesting, even though there's no pay.

I get the houses on Second Street and then it's time for the run to Rockwood Hill. I pedal clear back up to Adams Street, turn and rip down onto the Star Mill for all I'm worth, hitting that bridge at 200 miles an hour. (Okay, maybe it's more like 20-25, but it *feels* like 200.) I cut the turn onto the old white bridge and pump for the top of Rockwood Hill with everything I have. This time my old Columbia doesn't even wobble. Maybe I'm stronger now or maybe it's just the confidence of knowing I can make it, but for more than a month I've reached the top without having to get off and walk it. A quick look back over my shoulder to see what I've done, then I head for Mr. Lofgren's house.

He's on the porch waiting for me, just as he is every Saturday. "'Mornin', Alec," he calls as I hop off the bike to hand him his two papers.

"'Morning, Mr. Lofgren. What time is it?"

"'Bout 11:40," he says, which means I'll be home by noon easily.

"Anyone in the trailer yet?" I ask him this every Saturday.

"Not yet, but there's a family might be movin' in around Labor Day. They won't be able to take the paper, though. Anyone livin' back there'd be too poor to possess a pot to poop in."

That's his standard answer and it always brings a smile. It's one thing to overhear an adult using language like that or to have him cuss you out over something you do wrong, but to use it in such a casual way—like you're his equal and have heard it all before—that's somehow special.

No sign of Cap'n Andy this morning, so I'll save his extra for the next time I see him. I don't think he can tell the difference anyway. My last off-the-bike stop is Mrs. Phillips, who waits behind the counter with her knitting in her garage-turned-grocery store. I give her the paper, then plonk down two pennies for one of her big blue jawbreakers. I don't know where she gets them—no other store that I know of has them—but man, they are good! I put it in my pocket to save for later at the movies.

Going back down Rockwood Hill is a blast if there are no other cars heading up or down Western Avenue. I have to check both ways because the speed I build up will carry me into the far lane on the turn. When it's clear I pull my feet up and let it rip, imagining I'm Captain Joe McConnell diving his F-86 on an unsuspecting MIG-15. I'm a good four feet over the center line when I straighten the Columbia out and flash onto the Star Mill at the speed of sound—which in this case is a little over 25 miles an hour.

"Gotcha, ya commie rat!" I call to the doomed imaginary MIG.

Mom has a bowl of Campbell's tomato soup, a roast beef sandwich and milk ready when I sprint up the steps and bang the door shut behind me. "Goodness, Alec! Slow down!" she calls. "It's not even twelve yet. You have plenty of time, so go wash your hands—and run a comb through that hair! You look like a scarecrow!"

If I'm Captain McConnell, then Mom is General Ridgeway, and I know better than to argue with my superior officer. I take my time over lunch, but keep an eye on the clock over the stove. When it reads 12:25 and the soup, sandwich and milk are gone, I stand up, salute and say, "Permission to leave the table, Ma'am?"

"Yes, go on with you!" she says as she shakes her head. "Wait a minute! How much are you going to spend this afternoon?"

"Just a quarter, I think."

"Well, don't eat too much. I'm fixing a nice roast chicken for tonight, and I don't want you picking at your dinner."

"Yes, Ma'am!" I salute again and run for the door. Commanding officers can be a pain sometimes.

I ride back to Benny's to leave my bike in the stand the *Journal* boys use. Pietrowski is just heading out to do his route when I pull in. He's almost sixteen now and probably figures he's too old for the Saturday matinees. But I'm not. No sir!

Sprinting the two blocks back to Everett, I stop at Mom Jenkins' Popcorn Wagon for a big bag with extra butter. It sets me back a dime—but hey! I'm rich today. I still have twenty-four cents in my pocket, and that's enough for a whole afternoon's worth of food and fun. I race back across the street to the Lark Theatre and join a long line of kids waiting to buy tickets, which cost nine cents each.

There are two movie theatres on Third Street in 1953. The Morrison shows first-run, A-list films that get here two or three weeks after they've played in Portland. The Lark specializes in double features, less successful A-list pictures coupled with something from the B-list. Television and multiplexes will ultimately kill them off, but in 1953 they both thrive.

The Saturday matinee is a special event designed for kids twelve and under. Mr. Marmion, who owns both theatres, runs it in the spring and summer as a service to parents, and I think our folks pay him extra to do it. There's no Movietone News, no previews of coming attractions—just two low-budget B-list westerns and five or six cartoons, guaranteed to keep us entertained and out of trouble for about four hours.

I'd guess about two hundred of us cram our way into the Lark, and probably nine out of ten are boys. Mr. Marmion stations himself between the refreshment stand and the stairs to the balcony and takes our tickets. He frowns at my bag of Mom Jenkins' popcorn, but nods approvingly when I head for the candy counter.

Girls are allowed up in the balcony, and that's where all of them go, but it's off limits to boys. I guess there have been too many "accidents" involving coke or sticky pieces of candy or gum spilling over the rail onto kids sitting below. Four or five brave parent volunteers position themselves around the theatre to keep order.

I get myself two Clark bars and a small coke, which cost a total of fifteen cents, and move quickly to find a seat before all the good ones are taken. Most of the boys crowd down in front, but I keep to the back and well behind the overhang of the balcony. Janet Tabor could be up there, and I don't want to give her a target.

When we're all pretty well seated, Mr.Marmion begins the program by suddenly and dramatically killing the lights and simultaneously starting the first projector. A deafening "YAAAY!" goes up as Woody Woodpecker appears on the screen. He's followed by Bugs Bunny and then Tom and Jerry.

Then it's time for the first feature, which is always the better of the two. According to my journal, this one is *Duel at Silver Creek*, starring Audie Murphy. By the time it's over, I've gone through the coke, popcorn and one of the Clark bars. When the second set of cartoons comes on,I decide to save the remaining Clark bar for after dinner and have Mrs. Phillips' big blue jawbreaker with the second feature.

Gun Law Justice must be four or five years old. It's in black and white and features Jimmy Wakely, who is sort of a poor man's Gene Autry. I'm half-tempted to walk out after the first ten minutes or so, but I decide to stay and get my money's worth. It gets better, but not by much.

I'm home by 5:30 and Mom greets me with, "Well, how were the movies? You didn't eat too much junk, did you?"

"Nope." I show her the surviving Clark bar. "I saved this. Can I put it in the icebox?"

"Yes, and if you do justice to my cooking, you may have it after dinner. But not until you have something that's actually good for you."

No problem there. If Mom's roast chicken isn't the best in town, I've never heard of any better. After dinner Dad and I do the dishes, then I get my one hour of radio programs. I decide to go with *Gene Autry* at 7:30 and pick *the Lone Ranger* over *Gangbusters* at 8. Jimmy Wakely has a program on KOIN at 7, but I've heard enough of him for one day. At 8:30 Dad takes over the radio to listen to Guy Lombardo, and I head upstairs to bed. Five o'clock is going to roll around mighty early.

****

On the following Wednesday, Dad gets word from his new partner that he's passed the c.p.a. exam. The official results won't be out for a month, but Timmons knows someone who knows someone who checks the tests, and Dad finishes clear up near the top. Way to go, Dad!

To celebrate, Dad decides to take Mom out to dinner Saturday night and me up to see the Beavers play Los Angeles on Sunday. (Mom's love for baseball does not extend to doubleheaders.) Old Mrs. Walker from across the street comes over to stay with me—just in case of an emergency, Mom assures me. She adds that as soon as I'm twelve, I can stay up by myself. That will be great, but I don't mind Mrs. Walker. She's older than Grandma Fullerton, but still sharp upstairs. We turn off the radio and spend the evening playing the most popular new game of the year—scrabble.

The sky has already turned from black to gray, and a sliver of orange shows on the eastern horizon as I bump my bike down the front steps and head for the Flying-A station. By the time my papers are loaded it is nearly full daylight and barely cool enough to keep my jacket on. I take my time on the route, knowing that Mom and Dad will sleep in this morning after a late night together. I'm carrying forty Sunday editions and an extra bulldog in case I run into Cap'n Andy.

The Sunday Oregonian is already on the porch when I get home, so I take both papers into the kitchen with me and finish both sets of funnies by the time Mom and Dad show up at eight. Mom starts breakfast while Dad fixes coffee. I turn to the sports page and read the account of last night's game, which the Beavers lose, 9-4. Hopefully, they'll do better today.

"Take your glove," Dad tells me. "You never know. We might get lucky."

Mom fixes us a lunch even though we tell her it's not necessary. "I know what you'll do," she says. "You'll load up on hot dogs and pay forty cents apiece for them. That's outrageous! Well, I want Alec to have *something* that's actually good for him today."

It's not quite eleven when we head for Portland. Just north of Newberg we spot the first of a series of small red rectangles with white lettering. "Let's read 'em in sequence," Dad says. "You lead off."

So I take the first one. "Says Farmer Jones..."

"Who's bald on top..." Dad continues.

"I wish I could..."

"Rotate the crop."

"*Burma Shave!*" we both cry together.

"Write that one down for your journal," Dad says. "Someday those signs will just be a memory like your grandfather's steam engines."

It's one o'clock by the time we reach Portland, find a place to park near Vaughn Street and make our way into the ballpark. Red Adams, my favorite pitcher after Robin Roberts of the Phillies, will pitch the first game for Portland. Dad buys seats along the first-base line, just above and beyond the screen. "Keep that glove on," he warns me. "If Old Red's fastball is working today, the Angels could foul a few off this way."

Los Angeles gets a run in the top of the first on three straight singles after two men are out. Portland gets it right back in their half when Hank Arft blasts one onto the roof of an iron foundry just beyond the right field fence. "Just like Old Joe used to do, huh?" Dad cries as Arft crosses the plate. That brings a little twinge of sadness. "Old Joe" is Joe Brovia, the first baseball player I ever idolize, a pure slugger who would have a career in the majors if he could field. The Beavers trade him to Sacramento after the 1952 season.

Adams settles down and after four innings is nursing a 2-1 lead. The fifth becomes one of the most glorious experiences of my life. With two out, nobody on and an 0-2 count on the Angels' Gene Baker, Adams tries to sneak a curve by him. Baker gets just enough of it to loop it foul into the stands along the first base side—*my* side.

Even as it leaves Baker's bat, I *know* that ball is coming straight for me. But unlike the time the Crawford punter shanks the kick, I don't think anything because there's no time. I leap to my feet, throw out the glove and jump as high as I can—without even realizing I'm doing it.

Smack! The ball stings, even through the glove, but I hold on, and Dad grabs me by the back of my jeans as I come down with it. The crowd applauds and Red Adams actually smiles and waves at me. Then he gets Baker to tap an easy grounder to Eddie Basinski to end the top of the inning.

In the bottom half the Beavers load the bases on singles by Frankie Austin and Fletcher Robbe and a walk to Arft. Then Dino Restelli unloads them with a shot over the left-field fence. Wow! The first grand-slam home run I ever get to see, and a Portland Beaver hits it! Before the inning ends, they plate two more. Even Red Adams, a great pitcher but a lousy hitter, drives one in with a solid single. The final score is 13-3.

"Hope they saved a few runs for the second game," Dad says as he repacks the now-empty lunch basket. "Hey! Let's go see if we can get Old Red to sign that ball."

"Do you think he would?" I ask as we make our way down to the field.

"It never hurts to try," Dad replies.

I suppose it's impossible now for a boy to wander into a pro clubhouse, but things are different in 1953. A groundskeeper recognizes me and lets us down onto the field. "Hey, Clay!" he calls to the manager. "The kid who made the catch wants to see if Red will sign the ball. His dad's with him. Should I let 'em in?"

"Sure! Come on in, Son," the manager says as he shakes my hand. "I'm Clay Hopper. Red, you got time to sign a ball?"

"Yeah, if they have a pen." Dad produces one and Adams autographs the ball for me. "That was some grab you made, Kid," he tells me. "What position do you play?"

"Uh—third base," I manage to stammer. Lord! Here I am talking with someone famous—well, almost famous—and he's asking about me! "But I'm not on the team anymore, because I deliver the *Journal* after school."

"Do you now?" Adams says. "Hey, Marlowe! The kid who made that catch delivers your paper. You oughta interview him."

A tall man with silver hair strolls over and introduces himself as Marlowe Branagan. "I know who you are," I tell him. "I read your column just about every day."

"You do? Well, I saw that catch. Pretty spectacular."

"It was luck. He happened to hit it right at me. I didn't even have time to think."

"Your dad made a pretty good catch too—of you. He asks a few questions, then leaves to interview Restelli, who hit the grand-slam.

Meanwhile Dad comes up with a program, and I scramble around the clubhouse collecting autographs. I have Frankie Austin, the little Negro shortstop, and Eddie Basinski, the second baseman, sign together. "You two are as good as Pee Wee Reese and Jackie Robinson!" I tell them, and that brings a tremendous laugh from Austin.

"Hey, Eddie. You think I look like Pee Wee?" he asks.

"About as much as I look like Jackie," Basinski answers, and I realize I've just put my foot in it. Austin and Robinson are Negroes, and Reese and Basinski are white. But it's Reese and Austin who play shortstop, and Robinson and Basinski who are the second basemen. Jeez! How dumb can a guy get?

"Don't worry, Son," Basinski says. "I'll take it as a high compliment to be compared with Jackie Robinson of the Brooklyn Dodgers."

"Pee Wee ain't so bad either," Austin adds.

That brings a sigh of relief from me. Race is still a touchy subject in baseball in 1953. Negroes have only been allowed in the major leagues for six years—Jackie Robinson being the first to break the color line. A few teams are still all white. But Basinski and Austin are as good a second-short combination as you will find outside the majors.

Basinski is an interesting guy, and I wish I had the skills to sit down and interview him. He's thin and looks more like a teacher than a professional athlete. He wears glasses on the field, something that just isn't done in 1953. He's also a concert-level violinist who has played in symphony orchestras. Basinski is just back in the lineup after being out for several weeks when he gets beaned with a fastball. Batters don't wear helmets in 1953.

None of the players whose autographs I collect ever get more than a glance at the majors—though Basinski has already played two seasons with the Pittsburgh Pirates. Well, none except Red Adams, who has a long career as a pitching coach for the Dodgers when they move from Brooklyn to Los Angeles and break up the Pacific Coast League.

The old PCL consists of the Portland Beavers, Seattle Rainiers, San Francisco Seals, Oakland Oaks, Sacramento Solons, Los Angeles Angels, Hollywood Stars and San Diego Padres. It's been around since the turn of the century, but it will be reduced to a collection of farm teams when the majors start moving west in 1957.

"Hey Alec!" Branagan calls as Dad and I head back to the stands. "Make sure you read my column tomorrow."

Royce Lint, who pitches the second game for Portland, only gets four runs to work with. But it's enough, as the Beavers win 4-1 and climb to 44-42 in the standings. Dad and I stop for hamburgers on the way home to celebrate.

****

On Monday J. P. and the crew are waiting for me when I walk into the *Journal* room at Benny's. "Here's the celebrity now," J. P. says as he fires up his pipe.

"Huh?"

Ferraday hands me a sports page and says, "Check out Branagan's column on page four."

I open the section and find the column. Halfway down is a paragraph someone has marked.

The best defensive play of the afternoon was probably turned in by 11-year-old Alec Lewis, a **Journal** *delivery boy from Morrisonville, who made a leaping one-handed stab of a line-drive foul ball off the bat of the Angels' Gene Baker. The second-best grab was made by Henry C. Lewis, Alec's dad, who made a nice one-handed catch of his son just in time to keep young Alec from tumbling out of the grandstand.*

"Did they let you keep the ball?" Reed asks.

"Yeah, and Red Adams signed it for me!"

"Did you have a glove on?" Jill asks from the doorway.

"Sure I did. It still stung a bit."

"Hah! I bet Kenny coulda caught it barehanded!"

"Don't be such a little twerp," Rush tells her. "I bet you want to give him a great big kiss."

"Triple uck!" Jill exclaims and stomps back to the front.

"That always gets rid of her," Rush says. "Now tell us about the catch."

"It was really just luck. If he'd hit it a foot higher or a few feet to the left or right, I wouldn't have had a chance. Guess I was just in the right place at the right time."

So I become a one-day celebrity and get my name in the *Oregon Journal*. (*The Oregonian* doesn't mention me.) Of course, I cut out the column and put it in my own journal. Hey! It's the first time I ever see my name in print.

But before the year is over, I will see it again.

Coming events cast their shadows before them.

****

So the summer drifts along. Julius and Ethel Rosenberg, the spies who pass the secrets of the atomic bomb to Russia, finally go to the electric chair. An Air Force Globemaster crashes near Tokyo, killing 129 persons and making it the worst air disaster ever—a record that won't last very long. The St. Louis Browns lose 20 games in a row on their home field and get set to move to Baltimore.

But on July 27 we finally sign an armistice and end the war in Korea. "We have won an armistice on a single battleground, not peace in the world," President Eisenhower cautions. The United States suffers 162,000 casualties, including nearly 40,000 killed, in the process. The new boundaries in Korea are almost exactly where they were before the whole thing started.

Aunt Emma Snyder comes down to celebrate the Fourth of July with us and to inspect my journal. She likes what she sees and promises to have a pup for me, "if nature will cooperate."

But I'm worried about her. Senator McCarthy has expanded his hunt for reds to include the State Department, the army, Harvard University and the Methodist Church. I know that Mrs. Carruthers at the library is under pressure to remove books by suspected communists and "fellow travelers"—which I guess are people who aren't actually reds, but what some folks call "pinkos."

Aunt Emma is unafraid. "Just let that big jerk try to subpoena me," she tells us at dinner, "and I'll give him more than he ever bargained for. Truman was right. The only thing McCarthy carries around in that briefcase of his is a bottle of booze—and I'll bet it's not even a good brand!"

Her attitude surprises me a bit, and I ask her, "But Aunt Emma, don't you hate communism too?"

"I do, Alec. But I go after the real thing, not some poor deluded souls who said foolish things years and years ago like I did. Senator McCarthy wouldn't know a genuine communist if one came up and bit him on his fat bottom—and if he ever wants to question me, that's exactly what I'll tell him!"

"In that case," Dad says, "for both your sake and his, let's hope he doesn't."

****

A blistering Sunday afternoon in August, with the temperature hovering around ninety degrees. Okay, that's not hot by Arizona or Florida standards, but it is for the Pacific Northwest. The rain that we curse all through spring would be welcome now, but the skies remain cloudless, with only a slight haze from forest fires in the Cascade Mountains to the east and the Coast Range on the west.

But a circus has come to Morrisonville, and Dad and I are on our way out to see the show. (Mom doesn't like them.) It's not Ringling Brothers or Barnum & Bailey—just one of the dozens of small one-ring circuses that crisscross the United States during the early and mid 50's. They play one-day stands at the county seats of smaller rural counties—places like Morrisonville. We get one about once every two or three years, and I can never remember their names.

Dad and I drive out to the Shodeo Grounds (not a misprint—that's what they call it) a little over half a mile out Western Avenue beyond the Star Mill Bridge. We can see the dust from clear across the bridge. "Cheap outfit," Dad comments. They didn't even bother to wet the grounds first. Are you sure you want to spend your money out here?"

I am, although I can't say why. I have a feeling there's something out here that I need to see. It's like that same voice warning me the Crawford punter would shank the kick or that Gene Baker would hit that foul straight to me. Something is out here, and I need to find it.

I find two things and neither of them under the big top, which is actually pretty small. The first is an elephant, apparently the only elephant this circus owns, tethered by a chain around one leg to a stake driven into the ground.

"Criminy!" I say to Dad. "How do they expect a little stake like that to hold an elephant? One good jerk and he'd pop it right out of the ground."

"You and I know that, but it doesn't," Dad says. "I'll bet when it was just a calf—I think that's what they call baby elephants—they chained it to a big strong stake and let it try to pull its way free. All it could do was hurt itself, and it remembers now that pulling on the chain once caused it tremendous pain. So the chain holds it, even though it's fastened to something that could be pulled loose easily. I guess you can say the real power of a chain is what it can do to your mind."

That's one thing I remember.

Then there's the sideshow—freak show might be a better term. A series of little tents holds a collection of oddities, like The Incredible Tattooed Midget, World's Fattest Lady, Live Two-Headed Calf, and The Boneless Wonder Boy. None of them appeal to me, but down at the end of the line is a sign proclaiming The Terrible Killer Ape, and below it a picture of an enormous black gorilla frothing at the mouth and straining at the bars of its cage. There's no barker in front of the tent. Instead a tape recorder drones its message into a microphone, repeating it over and over into the hot August afternoon.

"Step right up, Ladies and Gentlemen, and see him in person! King Kong, the Killer Ape! Folks, it's actually him! The ape that killed the doctor's wife, and was allowed to live! Purchased by us at tremendous expense and on display here so that you can say that right here today you've seen a genuine killer! One thin dime, the tenth part of a dollar, lets you in to see this wonder of the animal and criminal world. Step right up, Ladies and Gentlemen..."

And on and on and on.

I pause in front of the tent and stare at the gaudy picture. Dad shakes his head and says, "You don't want to spend your money *here*, do you?"

"I've never seen a real killer before, Dad. Do you think...."

"I think you'll be disappointed, but it's your dime."

So I fork over ten cents to a tired-looking lady holding a cigarette with almost an inch of ash on the end and walk inside the tent. Another kid about my age and two adults stand in front of a cage staring at a brownish-black lump lying on a pile of straw. The air inside the tent is probably ten degrees hotter than outside, and it carries the sweetish-sick smell of decay.

"The damn thing's dead!" one adult says.

"Naw, it moved a minute ago," says the other. "There! I saw it breathe."

"Is it really a gorilla?" the kid asks. "It looks kinda small."

"I think it's just a big chimp, and we're just a bunch of big chumps," an adult replies.

"Do you think it really killed the doctor's wife?"

"I suppose it could have. You don't have to be big and powerful to kill someone. Just mean."

I move closer and stare at the brownish-black lump. Sure enough, I can see a slight movement as it breathes. Then a sharp acid odor fills the already pungent air.

"Jeez!" the kid says. "It's piddlin'!" The lump still doesn't move, but the smell is unmistakable.

"Piddlin' all over hisself," the adult agrees. "I've seen enough of this. Let's get outa here!"

They leave and so do I. When I tell Dad about it, he just nods and smiles.

"Forget the movies, Alec," he tells me. "Forget the radio programs and the comic books. *That's* what a murderer is really like."

I never learn the identity of the doctor or his wife, but maybe on that hot August afternoon I see my first real killer. I don't realize it, but it's like the time I get my name in the paper and watch a mediocre movie featuring a guy named Wakely. All these things are due to come around again.

Coming events cast their shadows before them.

Chapter Twelve: Bonnybelle

What's it like being an 11-year-old kid in a small Oregon town in 1953? Some things are pretty good. Neighbors know who you are and watch out for you. It's safe to go play in the park by yourself—unless you get Cap'n Andy mad at you. At Cozine Mr. Hunter and Mrs. Foster's worst discipline problems come from students chewing gum in class.

But there is a down side as well.

On August 20 the *Journal*'s main headline screams, REDS HAVE H-BOMB. All through 1953 we practice duck-and-cover drills at school, and one day Jack Klostermann, whose dad is a professor at the college, curls up into a tight little ball under his desk as we go through the drill. When the teacher asks him what he is doing, he replies, "I am practicing kissing my rear end goodbye, because Dad says that's what we all might as well do if the reds really drop one on us." He gets sent to the principal for that.

Then there is polio. The Salk vaccine is still a year or so away. March of Dimes posters and ads for the Sister Kenny Foundation show children dragging shriveled and disfigured legs around on braces or sitting in wheelchairs or lying paralyzed in huge iron lung machines. We're pretty lucky and escape the worst of it in the Northwest, so Benny is the only victim I actually know. But there are many others and sometimes it kills.

On July 15 the *Journal* runs a front-page story about a girl from Vancouver, Washington, who dies from polio complications just hours before her last and greatest wish is granted. She wants a television set, and workmen are trying to install one in her hospital room in Portland when she dies. At the time of her death she is sixteen years old and weighs forty pounds. It's a slow, nasty way for a kid—or anyone else—to die.

Okay, I don't get blown up or have to face some terrible disease. But I do have to go to the dentist twice a year.

Old Dr. Waggoner doesn't believe in giving anesthetic to any patient weighing less than a hundred pounds unless it is absolutely necessary, and he's the one who decides if it's necessary. I'm still a kid, so my opinion doesn't count. "Oh, it's just one little cavity. It won't hurt you all that much," he says as he prepares to drill. But his drill is old-fashioned and slow, and the pain is terrible. Maybe he thinks it will make me take better care of my teeth, and for a week or so afterward I brush the daylights out of them.

But in 1953 there is no fluoride in the water or in toothpaste, because lots of people think fluoridation is part of a communist plot to rot our brains. So we rot out teeth instead, and every six months I get tortured for an hour. No matter how hard I try, there's always that one new little cavity.

.

****

The summer of 1953 rushes by all too quickly. Soon we're in the middle of August, and the papers are running back-to-school ads. I get to go working the move list with J. P. about one Monday night each month, and I get enough orders for a new front bag to go along with the old side bags I buy from Scott. Dad advises me to take an extra every day—so long as I don't have to pay for it—know where the vacant houses are and watch for moving vans. "In your business the customer doesn't come to you," Dad tells me. "You have to go out and find him,"

On Monday, August 31, the *Journal* debuts a new comic strip by a young unknown artist. Apparently they're not sure if their readers will like it, so they keep it off the main comic page and run it separately on a different page each day. The young artist is Charles Schulz, and the strip is called *Peanuts*.

Mary Alice sends me a letter from Denver a couple of weeks before school starts. She tells me that Colorado is neat, but she feels sort of homesick for Oregon. Her letter gets a little mushy toward the end. She promises to come back sometime and walk down across the creek with me and signs off with "Love and kisses, Mary Alice." I write back to her, but I can't quite bring myself to use the same closing. I agonize over it for almost an hour before deciding on, "Your friend always, Alec."

But it's nice having a long-distance girlfriend. We can say what we want to each other, and there's no one around to laugh at us. Okay, maybe her brothers are laughing, but so what? They're over a thousand miles away.

One day at the library I ask Mrs. Carruthers if there is any way I could find out more about Mary Alice's Uncle Quentin. She mulls the question over, then tells me the best way would be to write to an expert. "I know just the person," she says. "His name is Arch Whitehouse. He was a fighter pilot himself in World War I, and he writes books and articles about aviation and combat flying."

"Yeah, but where do I find his address?"

"Finding out things like that is part of my job. I'll have it for you when you bring the paper tomorrow."" She does too. Mom helps me a bit with the letter and I mail it off, wondering if Mr. Whitehouse will reply and, if he does, if he can tell me anything about Quentin Patterson.

I wonder too about Mary Alice and everything that happens since that time last fall when I decide to help her

recite. Could she be the girl I'm fated to wind up with?
Then I meet Bonnybelle...

****

Tuesday, September 1, 1953. School starts in one more week. I'm trying to savor the last of the summer break as I do my route and start collecting again. I reach Rockwood Hill about four, knock on Mr. Lofgren's door, hand him his paper and ask if I can collect.

"Sure," he says. He hands me two dollars and adds, "Keep the nickel, but don't go yet. There's someone I want you to meet." He turns back to his kitchen and calls out, "Hey, Bonnybelle! Come on out and meet Alec."

A girl appears in the doorway, puts her hands on her hips, cocks her head to one side and glances at me like I'm a piece of merchandise someone is offering her. She's about my size, maybe an inch or so shorter, with dark blonde hair, gray-green eyes and a spatter of freckles across her nose and cheeks. She's wearing a pair of boy's jeans and a dirty t-shirt.

"Hey!" she says after a few seconds.

Even with just one word, I can catch the flat prairie twang in her voice and remember Mr. Lofgren's description: *too poor to possess a pot to poop in*. This girl is pure Okie migrant, but Dad and J. P. keep drilling me on being polite to everyone. So I give her a smile and say, "Hey yourself!"

"Are yuh the kid what delivers the papers?"

That bothers me a bit. Who is she calling a kid? I'm bigger and probably older than she is. "That's me," I say.

Mrs. Lofgren appears and says, "Mr. Alec Lewis, meet Miss Bonnybelle Wakely." Criminy! It sounds like she's introducing a duke to a duchess.

The last name doesn't register with me right away because I'm thinking, *Bonnybelle?* Girls in 1953 have names like Mary, Susan, Sharon, Linda, Judy, Jane or Alice. An Okie named Bonnybelle has two strikes against her before school even starts.

"See, we wanted her to meet you 'cause there's no one else 'round here that's her age," Mr. Lofgren continues. "We got some teenagers and a whole bunch of little kids, but nobody about eleven or twelve. That's your age, ain't it?"

I nod and manage to cough up a little sympathy for Bonnybelle. Just about all the kids in my neighborhood are three or four years older or three or four years younger than I am. But at least it's easy for me to get to my friends. Bonnybelle is stuck up on Rockwood Hill, and I bet she won't make many friends at school either. She'll have to go to Fox Glen, and all the other migrant kids will be at Cozine.

"Well, good to meet you," I say. "Gotta finish my route, Mr. Lofgren. Thanks for the tip."

I turn to go, but Bonnybelle says, "Hey! I'll come with yuh!"

"Sure, if you want," I say with a shrug. "Go get your bike."

"Ain't got none. I'll run alongside yuh."

I think, *sure you will.* Maybe Janet Tabor could run alongside a bike for three or four blocks, but no other girl I know could manage it—and I bet even Janet would be puffing and gasping after two or three hundred yards. But Bonnybelle surprises me. It will be the first of many surprises.

I have nine papers left to deliver after Lofgrens, and I plan to stop and collect at a couple of places, so I deliberately ride a little faster than usual. But Bonnybelle keeps pace alongside me and even manages to talk while she runs.

"Yuh do this ever' day, huh?"

"Yeah. Afternoons on weekdays, mornings on Sunday."

"How much do they pay yuh fer it?"

"A little over twenty bucks a month."

"Shoot! I kin make twenty bucks in a week. Twenty-five, if'n I work Saturdays an' the beans are good. Muh daddy kin make fifty in a good week."

Bonnybelle Wakely is starting to irritate me plenty. Not only can she run like a boy, she seems to think nothing about attaching herself to a townie, which is what the migrant kids call us—I think. Okies keep to themselves, and we tolerate them as long as they do. Anyway, I've seen kids like her out in the fields. They can work twice as hard as we can.

"Maybe so," I tell her, "but can you pick beans in December and January?"

"Nope," she admits. "That's why we moved to Old Man Lofgren's trailer. Daddy says he's a-gettin' too old fer all this roamin' 'round, an' Mama needs a place where she kin take better care of John Henry."

I'm about to ask who John Henry is when I hear a voice call, "Arric!" and Cap'n Andy comes waddling toward us. Bonnybelle squeals and turns to run away, but I grab her by the arm.

"No! Don't run—it's okay," I tell her. "He won't hurt you. He just wants his paper." I hand her Cap'n Andy's day-old copy and add, "Give him this, and I'll introduce you."

Bonnybelle holds out the paper like someone offering a hunk of meat to a hungry lion. Cap'n Andy snatches it and demands, "Who dat?"

"Mr. Slade, this is Bonnybelle. She's a nice girl and she won't ever tease you. Will you be nice to her?"

"She your friend?" he asks suspiciously.

Before I can think, I answer, "Yes, she's my friend."

"Okay. Won't hurt. What name?"

"Bonnybelle." She says it very carefully and tries to smile.

Cap'n Andy tries, but "Bobble" is the best he can do. Bonnybelle's smile widens, but she stops herself from laughing. "I'm right proud to meet yuh, Mr. Slade." She holds out her hand and doesn't wince very much when Cap'n Andy squeezes it. But after he waddles off with the paper, she turns to me and shivers.

"Man, he dang-near scared me right inta peein' muh pants!"

"Hey! He can't help the way he looks. But he won't hurt you if you're nice and don't tease him."

"Yeah? Well, he sure looks like an ol' boogerman to me. Are yuh double-dang-certain-fer-sure positive he won't come after me none if'n I'm yer friend?"

"I'm sure of it," I say, and again she cocks her head to one side and looks at me.

"Reckon I'd better be yer friend then," she decides, and we set off to finish the route together. Again she runs easily beside me and isn't even breathing hard at the end of two more blocks. I feel myself actually starting to like her, and I can't figure out why. She's nothing but an Okie, after all, and a girl as well. But when we reach Mrs. Phillips' store, I hop off the bike and she follows me inside.

"Hello, Alec," Mrs. Phillips says. "Who's your friend there?"

"Muh name's Wakely," Bonnybelle answers before I can speak up. "Miss Bonnybelle Wakely, an' I'm right proud to meet yuh, Ma'am."

"Bonnybelle?" Mrs. Phillips asks. "What an interesting name! I don't believe I've ever heard that one before."

"Yes, Ma'am. The Bonny is fer William Bonny, and the Belle is fer Belle Starr." She turns to me and asks, "Do yuh know who William Bonny was?"

It takes me a second,but I remember. "Billy the Kid, wasn't he?" All those Saturday westerns finally pay off.

"Hey! Yer right! Not many folk know that. What about Belle Starr?"

I shrug and guess. "Another outlaw?"

"Yer close. Muh daddy calls her the Bandit Queen of the Badlands."

"But why would your parents want to name you after two people like that?" Mrs. Phillips asks. I'm wondering the same thing.

"'Cause of the song ballads Daddy sung when he was a-courtin' Mama. Muh big brother was named fer Jesse James. These are his britches I'm a-wearin' right now."

"Doesn't your brother get mad when you wear his jeans?" I ask.

"Reckon he don't care no more," she says. "He's dead."

"Oh, how terrible!" Mrs. Phillips exclaims. Bonnybelle nods.

"Yes, Ma'am. He drowned last summer tryin' to swim across a river down by Salinas. Cramp took him." She says it calmly, as if losing a brother is just another unpleasant but not unexpected part of life. "He was only a year older 'n me, so they fit me purty good right now."

Mrs. Phillips just stares and shakes her head. I feel like I have to do something, so I take out the nickel Mr. Lofgren tells me I can keep. "Could I have two of the big blue jawbreakers, please?" I ask. Mrs. Phillips takes two of them out of the jar by her cash register and gives me a penny in change. "Here," I say and hand one to Bonnybelle.

"What's that fer?"

"Well, we're friends, aren't we? And friends share, don't they?"

"Reckon yer right." She grins and pops it in her mouth. I put mine in my pocket to save for after dinner. As we head back to my bike, she shifts the jawbreaker to her cheek and says, "Hey, Alec. Kin I ask yuh somethin'?"

"Sure."

"Do girls up here in Oregon hafta wear dresses to school?"

"Yeah, they do. Every day."

"Shoot! I ain't a-goin' then."

"You don't have any choice," I tell her. "You have to go to school and you have to wear a dress. What's wrong with that?"

"Well, in the first place, I ain't got but two. One's too big an' one's too small, an' we cain't get me another 'till Daddy gets a job an' gets paid. An' in the second place—here, hold this fer a minute!"

She takes the jawbreaker out of her mouth and sticks it in my hand. Then she puts her own hands over her head and flips sideways into a cartwheel. But halfway through she stops herself and balances on her hands for three or four seconds before rounding it off.

"Jeez Lou*eeze!*" I exclaim. "That's fantastic! Can you walk on your hands?"

"Only fer two or three steps," she says, but she kicks up onto her hands and manages five steps before flipping back over onto her feet. Then she takes the jawbreaker and pops it back in her cheek.

"Now pitcher me a-tryin' that in a dress!" she says. "'Specially when I only got three pair of drawers, an' one has a big ol' rip in the back. Shoot! Ever' boy in the class'd get a free look at muh butt!"

Now this is 1953, and girls—when they are around boys or adults—just don't talk like that. Maybe when they're by themselves, they can be as foul-mouthed as Dirty Dave, but no girl I know would mention her bottom or her underwear within earshot of a boy, especially one that she's known for only about ten minutes. This is my first conversation with a migrant kid outside of school (and then I only talk to them when I have to) and my first ever with an Okie girl. What kind of a world does Bonnybelle come from?

"Well, put a pair of shorts on under your dress," I suggest.

"Dagnabit!" she snaps at me. "I ain't got none!" Then her voice softens until she sounds like a teacher trying to explain something to a not-very-bright pupil. "I ain't got nothin', Alec. No bike, no purty clothes, no fancy store-bought toys..." Her voice cracks, and for a moment she looks like she's going to cry. Then she shakes her head and her whole face seems to harden.

"I know what's a-gonna happen. They'll start by makin' jokes about me. '*Bonnybelle has an awful smell!*' That's what they'd chant down in Californey last year. Then I'll get inta a fight an' get sent to the principal, an' after two or three times they'll kick me out. So why should I bother with it?"

That will happen, I realize. The other students will pounce on her like a school of hungry sharks. The teachers may try to protect her—for a while, at least—but she won't last. Girls can be a lot meaner than boys, and the odd one out always gets nailed. Just like poor Mary Alice. But Bonnybelle Wakely can't move to Denver and start over in some fancy private school.

Then I have an idea. It's a longshot, but it just might work.

"Follow me," I tell her. We march back into the store and I explain the situation to Mrs. Phillips. She puts down her knitting, picks up a pencil, leads Bonnybelle over to the doorway and places her against the frame.

"Stand up straight now," she says as she puts the pencil on Bonnybelle's head and makes a mark on the frame. "This is where I measure each of my grandbabies every fall," she explains. I look closely at the frame and see a whole series of similar marks running from two feet below to nearly a foot above the one she just makes. Each mark has a number and letter beside it.

"Just as I thought," she says as she examines the marks. "You're within half an inch of the line I made for Susan last year. She'll have shot up another three inches by now, so I'll bet my daughter is getting her new school clothes this very minute. Would you like to have her last year's things? I'll bet they would fit you just about perfectly."

For an instant I see a light in Bonnybelle's gray-green eyes. Then she shakes her head sadly. "Thank yuh, Ma'am, but I cain't. Daddy says we ain't a-gonna take no charity."

Mrs. Phillips is stymied, but only for a moment. "It wouldn't be charity if you worked for them now, would it?"

"What do yuh mean, Ma'am?"

"Lord love me, Honey! Do you know what a bother it is keeping a place like this clean? And I don't hardly dare get up on a ladder to dust the high shelves anymore. Now if you were to come in here for twenty or thirty minutes two or three times a week and clean the places I can't get to—well, those clothes could be your wages."

Bonnybelle's eyes brighten up again. "Reckon I might be able to do that, Ma'am."

"Then I'll call Susan's mother tonight and tell her to save them. You know, Louise up in Portland might have a few things that would fit you too. You come back tomorrow, Honey, and we'll get you all fixed up."

"Why'd yuh do that?" Bonnybelle asks me when we resume the route.

"I don't know. It just came to me that Mrs. Phillips might be able to help. She's always telling me about her grandkids, and how two or three of them are just about my age. I figured that if any were girls, they might have something they'd outgrown and you could use. You don't mind wearing things someone else has worn, do you?"

"Are yuh kiddin'?" she replies. "That's all I ever had. I ain't never worn nothin' store-bought new in muh whole life!"

I stop to collect at two more houses, getting paid at one and an *Aw, gee—can you come back tomorrow?* at the other. "Look at that!" Bonnybelle snorts when I trudge back to my bike. "Big ol' house an' a car in the garage an' they won't even pay the paper boy. Some folk are skunks!"

"They forget sometimes. I'll get it tomorrow."

"Bet if I ever had money, I'd remember who I was beholdin' to."

"I thought you said you made twenty dollars a week picking beans."

"Well, I do! But ever' cent Daddy an' me make hasta go fer food an' fer medicine fer Mama an' Uncle Roger. When Jesse was with us, we could put a little by. But ever since he drowned…" Her voice trails off and she shakes her head.

"Jeez! It must be awfully hard for you." Trust me to make some obvious, fat-headed remark at a critical time.

"Yuh don't know the half of it," she says as I sling the last paper but one onto a porch. "Where does that last one go?"

"That's for our house. Every paperboy delivers his own house last. I live clear down across the park. Look, Bonnybelle. If there's anything else I can do to help you..."

Again she cocks her head to one side and gives me that cool, appraising stare. "Reckon there might be," she says. "Could yuh give me a ride down the hill?"

"Sure. I'll take you all the way to town if you want."

"Naw. Just down the hill," she replies and hops on the carrier stand. I expect her to grab the back of the seat, but instead she wraps both arms around my waist and sticks her head between my shoulder blades. I check for cars and then push off.

It's a wilder ride than I plan on, since I forget to allow for the extra weight. Bonnybvelle is lighter than I am, but she still adds more than seventy pounds to the load my old Columbia carries. Halfway down Rockwood Hill we are flying, and I'm having doubts about making the turn at the bottom. I veer as far to the left as I can and hit the brakes as I go into a hard right turn. I hear Bonnybelle squeal as momentum carries us way over the center line on Western Avenue.

In fact, I come within a foot of smacking into a guardrail on the Star Mill and skid nearly twenty feet before I can stop. *There goes another dime's worth of rubber off the back tire.* Bonnybelle is still squealing, but her tone has changed from fear to joy.

"Whoo—*ee*!" she cries. "That's more fun than I had in weeks! Bet it's better'n a rolly-coaster!"

"Want to do it again?" I say with a bravado that I don't really feel.

"Naw. Reckon I better get back up that hill. Daddy'll skin me if'n he sees me way down here with a boy." She hops off the bike and gives me a quick hug. "I like yuh, Alec. Yer all right. See yuh tomorrer?"

"Sure," I say as she turns and starts running back up Rockwood Hill.

****

On Wednesday she's waiting for me at Lofgrens and we set off again. Cap'n Andy appears, and this time she hands him the paper without flinching. Cap'n Andy actually smiles at her and says, "Thanka, Bobble." Bonnybelle manages to keep a straight face.

"What do yuh reckon he does with it?" she asks after he waddles off.

"Man, I don't know. I don't think he can read it. Maybe he looks at the pictures."

"Well, I reckon he's okay an' I'm safe from him now, an' I thank yuh fer that. But that face of his is sure ugly enough to scare the pee-dottles outa yuh, ain't it?"

I'm not sure what a pee-dottle is, but I agree.

Mrs. Phillips is beaming when we walk into her store. "Bonnybelle!" she cries. "I've got some really nice things for you, and there's more on the way. Would you like to see them?"

"Thank yuh kindly, Ma'am. I'll be back soon as I help Alec finish his route."

I think, *she's putting off something that important just to help me?* The gesture really touches me, so I pull out another nickel and ask for two more big blue jawbreakers.

"Ah, Alec! Having a girlfriend can get mighty expensive!" Mrs. Phillips teases as she hands them to me.

"No, she's not…That is…I don't think…"

"'Course I am!" Bonnybelle exclaims as she stuffs the jawbreaker into her cheek. "Whassamatter? Don't think I'm good enough fer yuh?"

"No, it's not that," I say as we head back outside. "It's just that I haven't asked—"

"Then ask, dagnabit!"

So I swallow hard and ask Bonnybelle Wakely if she will be my girlfriend. "'Course I will!" she says as she throws her arms around my neck and kisses me on the cheek. I don't know how to react because no girl at Cozine would act this way. They'd probably giggle and smirk and run to tell their friends. Well, Mary Alice wouldn't, but she's gone now.

I try to kiss Bonnybelle back, but she pulls away. "Lips come later," she tells me. "Yuh don't get everythin' all at once." Apparently she knows more about this business than I do.

But how do I get myself trapped into having an Okie for a girlfriend? If anyone ever finds out, I'll never hear the end of it. They will too. You can't keep a secret in a small town.

I let her sling the last four papers while I stop to collect. The people who put me off on Tuesday pay up, and Bonnybelle is satisfied. "Good thing they did or I'd a-let 'em know about it!" she tells me.

When we reach the edge of Rockwood Hill, she hops on the carrier stand and wraps her arms around me as if being my girlfriend automatically entitles her to a free ride down to the Star Mill. What the heck—maybe it does. I push off and she squeals all the way down, but it's more from joy than fear. This time I allow for the extra weight and control the speed a bit better. Again we come dangerously close to the guardrail, but I don't have to slam on the brakes and skid. The momenturm carries us clear across the bridge before we coast to a stop. Then I turn around and pedal us slowly back to the foot of Rockwood Hill.

"Man, that was great!" she says as she hops off the bike. "I gotta git, Alec. See yuh tomorrer." She gives me another peck on the cheek and runs back up the hill.

****

On Thursdays the papers are too large to be folded for throwing, and I have more collecting to do. So I'm probably fifteen or twenty minutes late reaching Rockwood Hill. There's no sign of Bonnybelle at Lofgren's, and I feel vaguely hurt by her absence. But when I reach Mrs. Phillips' store, she's waiting for me inside.

"Lookee what I got!" she cries as she dances out from behind the counter. She's wearing a gray skirt and a white blouse with lace at the collar. Her shoes look new too, and Mrs. Phillips has done something to her hair. "Been waitin' half an hour to show yuh all this. What took yuh so long?"

I explain about the larger papers and the collecting and she says, "Reckon it's all right, then. But whattayuh think of muh new duds? Reckon I look as purty as them townie girls now?"

"No," I tell her, and her smile vanishes.

"You look better!" I add quickly, and her whole face brightens up again as if someone switches on a light behind her eyes. "Hey! *You're* a townie now, and they're all going to be jealous of you."

"Whoo-*ee!* Them jealous of *me?* That'll be somethin' new!" she says as she spins around. "Alec, I ain't never worn so much lace in all muh life! See, it's here on the blouse, an' here on muh slip." She pulls the skirt up a few inches to show me. "I ain't ever even had me a slip afore, never no mind one with lace on it. I even got lace on muh new drawers!" She grins and adds, "But I ain't a-gonna show yuh *them,* so yer just gonna hafta take muh word on that. And yuh know what's even better?"

"No. What?"

"Miz Phillips got me some shorts to put under muh skirt, so I kin cartwheel an' walk on muh hands as much as I want an' not have muh bee-hind showin'. Hey! Finish up them papers and get on back here. I'll have muh new jeans on then, and yuh kin take me down the hill again."

I finish up and collect from a couple more houses, and by the time I get back, Bonnybelle is waiting outside the store. She's wearing a clean white pullover shirt and a pair of girl's jeans this time. (I can tell because they zip up the side and not the front.) "Time's a-wastin'!" she cries as she hops on the carrier stand and grabs the back of the seat.

When we reach the top of Rockwood Hill, she wraps her arms around my middle and jams her head against my back. I think, *this girl is getting just a little too confident. Let's see if I can shake her up a bit.*

I keep the bike in the right lane all the way down and don't use the brakes until Bonnybelle starts to squeal. Then I give them a quick jab and swing the old Columbia to the left. Her squeal becomes a scream of pure terror when she realizes we're turning the other way, and we go clear off the pavement onto the gravel shoulder before I can straighten out and rip off down Western Avenue. By the time we coast to a stop, I can feel her arms squeezing the breath out of me and her own breath coming in short, sobbing gasps.

"What yuh tryin' to do?" she gasps. "Scare me inta messin' muh new britches?"

"Just thought you'd like to see what the other way was like," I say as we ride back. "Want to try it again?"

"Okay, but kin yuh warn me which way yer gonna go?"

"Isn't it more fun if you don't know?"

"Well...maybe." I can't see her face with her head pressed up against my back, but I know she's grinning again. "I kinda like a *leetle* scare once in a while."

But we don't get the chance to try it again. We're walking the bike back up Rockwood Hill when an old rattletrap of a car comes up behind us and I hear a sharp voice call, "Bonnybelle!"

Bonnybelle freezes and her face turns pale. "Oh man! I'm in fer it now!" she gasps. "That's Daddy, an' he's caught me a-comin' back up the hill with a boy!"

"Do you want me to come with you and explain—"

"No! That'll make it worse! Get on home, an' I try an' see yuh tomorrer."

"But if I told him it was my idea—"

"No! Git!" She practically screams it at me and runs on up the hill to where the car sits with its engine idling. I expect her to get in, but instead she leans in at the window and talks with the driver for a moment. I'm too far away to hear what they're saying. Then she steps back and the car drives away. Bonnybelle takes off after it as fast as she can run, while I coast back down Rockwood Hill and head for home.

****

I really don't expect to see Bonnybelle on Friday, but she's waiting on Lofgrens' porch for me to come by. "I cain't go down the hill with yuh no more till Daddy says it's okay," she tells me. "But Mama says I kin go with yuh 'round to Miz Phillips' place if'n yuh come in an' meet her first. Will yuh do that fer me, please?"

"Sure," I say and follow her over to the trailer. *Sheesh!* I think when we step inside. How does more than one person live here? The whole thing can't be any bigger than my room. A woman sits on a tattered sofa, watching a little boy who can't be more than two as he plays with a broken toy on an old rug. Bonnybelle, her dad and maybe her uncle have to find space here too.

"This is muh mama, Alec. Mama, this here is Alec. He's a real nice boy, and yuh don't hafta worry none about me when I'm with him."

"I—I'm pleased to meet you, Mrs. Wakely." I say it automatically as she lifts her eyes to look at me, but I'm not sure if I mean it. She is a woman who must have been beautiful once, but she's thin and pale like the newsreel pictures they show of the soldiers held prisoner by the North Koreans. Her face is deeply lined, and her eyes have the haunted look of someone who has seen death pass by. Yet she can't be much more than thirty. Looks don't last when you're a migrant.

"Uh-huh." She says it as if talking is almost more work than she can manage. "Yuh kin go 'round up here with him, if'n yuh want. But not down the hill till yer daddy says so." Then her eyes drop back to the little boy playing on the rug.

There are two doors, one at each end of the room, and I hear a noise behind one. "That's Uncle Roger in the bathroom," Bonnybelle says. "He don't much like to be 'round company. Daddy ain't here right now. C'mon, let's go."

She says nothing more until we're a hundred yards down the gravel street. "Not much of a place, huh?" she finally comments.

"I guess not." Criminy! What else can I say?

"But we ain't gonna hafta stay here fer long, Alec. Daddy's just got hisself a job down at O'Dell's Garage. See, Mr. Lofgren told him Mr. O'Dell said one of his mechanics hadta quit 'cause he got drafted. So Daddy went down an' asked fer the job, an' O'Dell gave him the test an' he passed. 'Course, I knew he would."

"What kind of test?"

"See, they have this here ol' heap in the back of the shop. Got a whole buncha things wrong with it. Mr. O'Dell said if'n Daddy could get it runnin' in two hours, he could have the job. Shoot! Only took Daddy twenty minutes! He was on his way back to tell us when he saw me a-comin' back up the hill with yuh."

"Uh, Bonnybelle, did you get in a lot of trouble?"

"I got a lickin', but it warn't a bad one."

"What do you mean it wasn't bad?"

"Well, yuh saw me a-talkin' to Daddy by the car, remember? He said he was a-gonna drive on home and then start countin', an' I'd get me one lick fer ever' second he counted afore I got there."

"Jeez! How high did he count?"

"He said nine, but I was a-countin' in muh head as soon as I saw him stop, an' I was clear up close to twenty by the time I got there."

"Yeah, but even nine…" I nearly shudder at the thought.

"Hey! It warn't so bad. He didn't use his belt, an' I didn't hafta pull down muh pants. He just dusted the seat of muh jeans with his hand. I squalled a bit just so's he'd know I could feel it, but it didn't hurt hardly none at all."

"Yeah, but if I could have explained—"

"Uh *uh!* Supposin' he was a-comin' back with bad news? Then he'd a-took his belt to me, like as not, an' I woulda hadta pull muh pants down right there in fronta yuh! That's why I was yellin' at yuh to git. I don't plan on havin' yuh see muh bee-hind fer awhile yet!"

I don't know what to say to that, but Bonnybelle just shrugs. "It's all right now. Daddy ain't mean like he was afore he stopped drinkin'. He was so happy about a-gettin' that there job that he got out his guitar last night, an' him an' me sang song ballads an' gospel for Mama an' John Henry an' Uncle Roger."

"John Henry's the kid on the floor? He's your little brother?"

"Yep. He'll be two next month. Betcha he'll be a singer too. He was a-tryin' to sing with us last night. Jesse an' Amy Rose never could sing a lick."

"Who's Amy Rose?"

"Muh little sister. She died 'bout two years ago."

"Sheesh! You've lost a brother *and* a sister?"

"Yeah. There shoulda been six of us. Mama had two that was stillborn. After John Henry, the doctors fixed her so's she cain't have no more. Said havin' another might probably kill her."

There's nothing I can say to that, so I just shake my head. Her world *is* totally different from mine.

"But Alec, it's all a'gonna be better now. Daddy's got hisself a steady job, an' purty soon we'll get a real place, all our very own! Mama'll get stronger an' she'll get some steady work, an' I'll take care of John Henry." Her voice gets higher and faster as she pictures the scene in her head.

"We'll get Uncle Roger inta the V.A. place up in Portland, an' they'll make him all better again! An' I'm a-gonna do real good in school this time, 'cause none of the other kids are a-gonna tease me about muh clothes—thanks to you an' Miz Phillips!" Bonnybelle's eyes are shining now, and I could swear that even her dusting of freckles seems to glow. "She says she's a-gonna 'dopt me as one of her grandbabies! What do yuh think of that?"

"Pretty neat." That's all I can trust myself to say.

"Reckon I got me 'bout the bestest boyfriend in the world too," she says as we reach the store.

"Then I guess we'd better celebrate. How about I get us a couple more jawbreakers?"

"Reckon that sounds like a purty good idea!"

Chapter Thirteen: Two Dinners

T*uesday, September 8:* We're now officially in the sixth grade, and there are no more bigger guys lording it over us. For one full glorious year, *we* are the big cheeses! And we will have men for teachers too! We all march into Mr. Hunter's room, line up against the walls—boys on one side, girls on the other—and count off, one-two, one-two, to see who goes into which room.

As the count finishes, Mr. Hunter looks at me and asks, "Alec, what number are you?"

"Two, Mr. Hunter."

"Janet, what are you?"

"Two."

"Trade places with Carole. You're now a one." Apparently Mrs. Foster has warned Mr. Hunter and Mr. Jackson about the bad blood between Janet and me.

I've promised Grandpa Fullerton that I will try to patch things up as quickly as I can, so I catch up to Janet after we march outside for the first recess of the day. (Yes, in 1953 we actually march, two abreast and in step.) This time I manage to remember my little speech.

"Janet, I'm really sorry about the way things ended last spring, and I'd like to make it up to you. So I'll play you any game, anywhere, anytime."

Janet gives me a smile of pure malice. "That's fine with me," she says. "The game is stretch. The place is here. The time is now. Got your knife?"

I pat my right front pocket and we move out onto the field, sizing each other up as we face off. I've grown a bit during the summer, but Janet seems to have grown even more. In fifth grade she's about an inch taller than I am, but now it's closer to two. And are my eyes playing tricks or does she now have two little bumps on the front of her blouse? Larry Dale notices me staring and stage-whispers, "Hey Alec! You think it's Janet or do you think it's kleenex?"

If he means to rattle Janet with this, It doesn't work. She pulls her knife from her skirt pocket and casually opens it. "You want to go first?" she asks in a tone that suggests it won't make any difference.

"No, you lead off," I reply, and she sticks her knife about one foot out. I stick mine about six inches farther and she stretches out to it. She's wearing a flared skirt, so doing the splits will be no problem for her. But I have a little surprise in store.

A crowd quickly gathers around us. Apparently word has gotten out that Janet and I are enemies, and this is more than just a friendly match. We play it slowly, each of us stretching out no more than a few inches at a time. Neither of us misses. Finally Janet drops down into the splits, gives me her *I gotcha now* smile and sticks her knife right beside her foot and an inch or so back from her toe. Her message is obvious—*I can go beyond this point, and you can't even reach it!*

But she has left it just a little too short. If I do the splits, I *can* reach it, and that's just what I've been working on every day since my talk with Grandpa Fullerton. It's going to hurt a bit. I can't hold it as long as Janet. But I stretch out all the way down, flex my toe and tap the hilt of Janet's knife. *Okay, Tabor. Now who's got whom?*

"Mr. Hunter!" Claudia cries. "Come and look! They've both got their bottoms clear down on the ground!"

Mr. Hunter takes a look, pulls Janet up with one hand and me with the other, and then raises both our arms. "I declare the game a draw, and you are both co-champions of the sixth grade at Cozine School," he says. "Now pick up your knives and come with me."

He takes us back to his classroom and sits us facing each other across a table next to his desk. "I don't know what's going on between you," he tells us. "I'm not sure that you know either. I do know that you are two of the brightest and most talented pupils in the whole school. But you're also the most stubborn, and I am not going to have you at each other's throats all year. So you're both going to sit there and talk things over until you can come to a peaceful solution. And you'll be in here every recess until you do—even if it takes all the way to Christmas. Now both of you give me your knives."

"Mr. Hunter!" Janet protests. "You don't think we'd—"

"Of course not," he says. "But I know you'd both like to have them back. And you can, as soon as you work things out. Now I'm going back outside. You can report to me this noon on how things are going. I don't expect you to become best of friends. I'll settle for a truce like the kind we have in Korea."

And with that he walks out and leaves us facing each other across the table.

Janet and I sit without looking at each other for several seconds. I can tell she's fuming, and I'm not in a very good mood either. Finally our eyes meet and she says, "How do we do this?"

"I'm not sure," I say. I'm trying to remember Grandpa Fullerton's advice. "Janet, can I ask you something?"

"Why not? There's nothing else to do."

"That first time you challenged me—why did you do it?"

"Because I thought I could beat you. And I did too. Remember?"

"Yeah," I admit. "But did someone dare you to come over and challenge Larry and me?"

"Well, yes. Claudia did."

"And what about that lovebird game with Mary Alice? Was that Claudia's idea too?"

"Yeah. You made me show off my underpants to you and the other boys, remember?"

"Hold it! I didn't *make* you do anything. You could have given up any time."

"And admit you could beat me? The only reason you even got a tie today was because I didn't know you could do the splits. What did you do, practice all summer?"

"That's right. But Janet, I never looked at your drawers."

"Maybe or maybe not. But Old Big-Mouth Larry sure did! Remember what he said? 'Hey Janet, you look really nice in blue!' Cripes! I wanted to punch him right in the mouth—and you too!"

"Why didn't you?"

"Claudia said it would be better to use Little Miss Peepants. She said that since you gave Larry a look at my undies, I should give him a look at your girlfriend's. That way you'd get mad and get in a fight with him, and he'd do the punching for me. Poetic justice, she called it. Almost worked, too."

"Yeah, but didn't you feel bad about pretending to be friends with Mary Alice and then double-crossing her?"

Janet's head droops. "Yes," she admits. "Not right when it happened, but later on I felt like a louse. But hey! What about that time you sucker-tripped me and then lied about it?"

"I felt terrible, Janet. When I saw how hard you hit, and you weren't moving, I just wanted to crawl into a hole and pull it in after me.." I swallow hard and then make my pitch. "Janet, I reckon we both picked an old tomcat up right by the tail."

"Tomcat? What are you talking about, Alec? You sound almost like an Okie."

So I tell her about Grandpa Fullerton and his advice (leaving out the part where he has to change his name and leave home). "And that's what he meant about picking up the cat by the tail," I conclude. "We were both played for suckers, Janet. We're stuck in here while Claudia's probably out there laughing herself silly at the mess we're both in."

Janet is every bit my equal in the brains department, and she catches the point quickly. "Why, that scheming little—dang! I can't say it in front of you!" She jumps to her feet and paces rapidly back and forth. "But when I get my hands on her..."

"Don't, Janet! You'll just get yourself in more trouble. Let's work together. We'll think of something."

Janet is still seething, but she sits back down. "All right," she agrees. "We'll both get back at her sooner or later." She holds out her hand. "Truce?"

"Truce," I say and we shake on it. "Can I tell you one more thing?"

"What?"

"I wish they'd let you play on the football team. You'd be a great wingback."

"Why thanks, Alec." Then she finally smiles. "Now let me tell you something. I don't put kleenex in my bra—but Claudia does! You can tell *that* to old Big-Mouth Larry!"

****

Bonnybelle is waiting for me when I drop off the paper for Mrs. Phillips. She's wearing her brother's jeans and has the old t-shirt on again, a rag tied around her head and a duster in her hand. I ask her how her first day at Fox Glen goes, and she cocks her head to one side as she considers the question.

"Good an' not so good," she says after some thought.

"What was not so good?"

"They put me back in fifth grade again. But it ain't 'cause I'm dumb! They said it's 'cause I missed so much the last couple years. Shoot! I'm half a head bigger'n everyone else in the room."

"Hey! Then they won't pick on you."

"That's what's good! Nobody's said nothin' bad 'bout me! And Miz Marshall says I'm really purty smart, an' if'n I work real hard all year an' don't miss too much, she'll skip me on to seventh grade come next spring. Then we can go to junior high together. Whattyuih think of that?" Again her whole face seems to light up.

"That would be great!" I say, and I mean it.

"'Fraid I cain't ride down the hill with yuh today, Alec. Gotta help Miz Phillips get rid of these durn ol' cobwebs so I kin pay off muh new duds. Anyhow, Daddy ain't met yuh yet. But yuh know what?

"What?"

"Soon as I get these here clothes worked off, Miz Phillips is gonna pay me cash money fer helpin her—an' yuh know what I'm a-gonna do then?" Before I can answer, she tells me. "I'm a-gonna buy them big ol' blue jawbreakers fer yuh! Whattyuh think of that?"

"That would be great!" I tell her, and again I mean it.

****

All the way back home a memory plays around the edges of my mind. Finally it crystallizes and I can see it again. I'm back in the third grade, and Davy Scroggins, ugly little Davy with the mohawk haircut, is out on the playground with me and telling me how he wishes he could live like me after I describe an ordinary dinner we would have that night. I remember how I want to invite him over to share it with us, but can't work up the nerve.

Well, this time I will.

I wait until Mom and I are setting the table that night, and then I ask, "Would it be all right if I invited a friend over for dinner sometime?"

"That would be fine," she says. "Is it one of your classmates?"

"No. It's someone who lives on my route."

"All right. Pick a time next week. What's his name?"

"Uh, it's not a him. It's a her."

"My goodness!" she says as she smiles and ruffles my hair. "What happened to the great love affair between you and Mary Alice?"

"She's in Denver now. I don't think she could come a thousand miles for dinner. This girl's name is Bonnybelle, and she goes to Fox Glen."

"Well, she really must be something if you're smitten enough to want to invite her to dinner. Find out what she likes, and I'll try to fix it."

So the next afternoon at Mrs. Phillips' I swallow hard and ask Bonnybelle if she'd like to have dinner at our place sometime next week. "Oh man! I'd sure like to!" she says. "But I'll hafta ask Mama an' Daddy, and Daddy won't let me till after he's met yuh. Kin yuh come back in 'bout half an hour? He's most times home by then."

"Sure. I can do that. Hey, if you can come, what would you like to have?"

"Whattyuh mean?"

"Mom said she'd fix your favorite thing. What is it?"

Bonnybelle looks at me as if I've just offered her the treasures of Aladdin's Cave. "Yuh mean, I could pick anythin' I wanted?"

"Just about. I think Mom would draw the line at lobster, but—"

"Ugh! I seen pitchers of them. Ugly critters with big ol' claws. Nope, if'n I could have anythin' I wanted, it'd be fried chicken with smashed taters an' plenty of gravy!"

"What else?"

Again she cocks her head to one side and stares at me. "Are yuh makin' fun of me?" she asks.

"No. I promise I'm not. Mom's a terrific cook. We'd have a vegetable, maybe a salad and dessert too."

"Alec, please! Don't say no more!"

"Why? What's wrong?"

"Ever' since we moved up here an' I met yuh and Miz Phillips, it's like I've been a-livin' in a dream, an' I'm just so scared I'm a-gonna wake up an' find I'm back at some ol' camp somewheres, and nothin's never gonna change!"

Her chin quivers. Then, suddenly, her whole body starts to shake. I don't know what to do, but Mrs. Phillips comes to the rescue. She takes Bonnybelle in her arms and rocks her gently. "Poor little thing!" she croons. "You probably haven't had a good cry for ages. That's all right, Honey. Just let it all come out."

She turns to me. "Alec, finish your route and then come back over to Lofgren's at about 5:30. Meantime, I'll walk her back home and have a word with her mama."

"Oh no, Miz Phillips!" Bonnybelle sobs. "You don't gotta close up yer place on acounta me!"

"Don't fret about that, Honey. I doubt if I'll have more customers today anyway."

So at 5:30 (roughly, since I still don't have a watch) I pull my bike up in front of Mr. Lofgren's house. The old rattletrap of a car is parked on the street in front, which means that her dad is in the trailer with her, and I'm going to have to face him. Since I've never had a clear look at Bonnybelle's father and have only heard him yell one word—her name—my mind conjures up all kinds of images, and none of them very pleasant.

But I'm wrong again. Ray Wakely is a tall, lanky man with steel-gray eyes, and the same darkish-blonde hair that Bonnybelle has. The face is sharper, though, with the features looking like they've been chiseled from very hard rock. When he speaks, the words come out in a low, musical baritone, with just a hint of Oklahoma or North Texas in them.

"So yer the young feller muh Bonny Girl's so crazy' bout, huh?"

Bonnybelle jumps in before I can reply. "Daddy! I ain't never said nothin' like that!" Her eyes are still red-rimmed from crying, but her voice is back under control.

"Yuh don't have to, muh Bonny Girl," he says as he puts an arm around her shoulder and she snuggles against his chest. "Yuh got that same look yer Mama had when she first clapped eyes on me."

"Never no such thing!" she protests, but not very convincingly. Her father just laughs and squeezes her a little tighter.

Somewhat embarrassed, I look away and catch sight of another man standing in the doorway of the cramped little trailer. The moment our eyes meet, his drop and he looks down at his shoes.

"Gotta get me some cigarettes," he mutters. "Ray, you got a quarter I could borrow?"

"Don't reckon I'll ever see the return of it, Roger," Ray Wakely says as digs a coin from his pocket. "But here yuh go." He tosses the quarter to Roger, who snatches it out of the air and then slips back outside.

"That's muh Uncle Roger," Bonnybelle explains. "He's Mama's older brother. What about it, Daddy? Could I please go over to Alec's house fer dinner sometime?"

"Now just you rein in a minute, muh Bonny Girl. I ain't heard this young feller speak a word about it yet." The steel-gray eyes look me over as he cocks his head to one side, just like his daughter does. "Yer name is Alec, right?"

"Yessir. Alec Lewis. I deliver the *Journal* up here."

"But yuh don't live up here?"

"Nosir. I live down on Adams Street, over on the other side of the park."

"What does yer Daddy do?"

"He's a certified public accountant, Mr. Wakely." I say it proudly. I can see that Bonnybelle loves and admires her father. Well, I love and admire mine too. "The firm's name is Timmons & Lewis."

Ray Wakely cracks a smile and ruffles Bonmnybelle's hair the same way my mother plays with mine. "Oh my!" he says in a gentle, laughing tone. "The son of a gentleman! Looks like yer fixin' to move up in the world, muh Bonny Girl."

"Please, Daddy! Don't speak mean 'bout Alec. He's been real nice to me."

"I won't do that 'cause he does seem like a purty nice boy. But Bonnybelle, if'n yuh go over to dinner at his house, then we're beholdin' to 'em, and how kin we ever pay 'em back?"

"I done thought of that, Daddy. Miz Lofgren says I could have him over to her place, an' I'd help her to cook an' clean up. Then yuh and Mama could come over with yer guitar and sing some song ballads for 'em. Alec, did yuh know Daddy's a cousin to Jimmy Wakely?"

"Bonnybelle!" Ray Wakely's tone sharpens. "We don't know that fer sure. Maybe I'm 'bout a second or third cousin, but that'd be as close as I come."

"But yuh kin sing as good as he can—maybe even better! Yuh ever heard Jimmy Wakely sing, Alec?"

"Yeah. I saw one of his movies this summer."

"Well, just wait till yuh hear Daddy! An' I sing harmony with him too! Sometimes we kin get Mama to join us. Then I sing lead, Daddy does the low harmony and Mama sings the high!" Again the excitement seems to light up her whole face. "What about it, Daddy? Could I go? Purty please with cream an' sugar?"

Ray Wakely cracks another smile and kisses his daughter on her forehead. "Yuh got yer heart set on this, ain't that so, muh Bonny Girl? Well, if'n it's all right with Alec's mama and daddy, it's all right with me. But yuh'd better mind yer manners!"

"Don't yuh worry none 'bout that, Daddy. Miz Phillips is a-learnin' me how to act just like a lady!"

"Well, reckon I'm glad to hear it. There's one more thing.

Alec?"

"Yessir?"

"Be real careful when yuh give muh Bonny Girl rides down that hill! Yuh hear?"

****

Mom checks her calendar and decides that Sunday the 20th would be a good day. I groan at the idea of having to wait so long, but Mrs. Phillips is happy. It will, she says, give her time to alter a party dress that her granddaughter in Portland has outgrown. It will also be time enough for her to give Bonnybelle a few lessons in party manners. I see them at the store a couple of days before the dinner and ask how she's doing.

"Purty dang good!" she tells me. "I ain't a-gonna make no more mention of muh bee-hind ner muh drawers, 'cause real ladies don't talk 'bout things like that."

"They don't say *ain't* either," Mrs. Phillips reminds her.

"Dang! That's a-gonna be awful hard, Miz Phillips. But I'll keep a-tryin'!"

****

Dad is being secretive about something, and he won't tell us what it is. He sits at the dinner table with one of those little half smiles on his face—the kind that say, *I know something that you don't!* On the very day we have Bonnybelle over for dinner, he springs the surprise. "Got an errand to run," he says as he drops us at home after church. "Be back in a few minutes." He drives off in the old DeSoto and returns with a brand-new, dark blue 1953 four-door Pontiac sedan.

"Henry!" Mom exclaims. "I thought we were going to wait..."

"Couldn't pass it up," Dad says. "Bud Patterson called from Denver and told the dealer to give us a real sweetheart bargain. It actually cost less than the model we were looking at, plus it has an automatic transmission, power steering—

and a radio, Alec."

"But are you sure we can afford—"

"We can't afford not to," he says. "Alec, I think old Bud might be having an attack of conscience over the way he treated you and Mary Alice. Any rate, he actually took a small loss on this deal. And Timmons has been after me to get rid of that old DeSoto—bad for the firm's image. So, Alec, what say we go pick up Miss Bonnybelle in a brand new chariot?"

"Hold on!" Mom says. "I want a ride in it first. Anyway, we won't be getting Bonnybelle for hours yet. Alec," she says to me, "I guess I'm going to have to start giving you advice about dealing with girls. The first rule is this: *never* show up early for a date and make the girl rush to get ready."

So we cruise around town for half an hour. I want Dad to take it out on 99W and open it up, but he says no. "We're not supposed to take it up over forty till we put a hundred miles on the odometer. Bad for the engine." I look at the odometer and groan—33 miles. "We'll have to take really good care of this little beauty," Dad says as he pulls over to let Mom have a turn behind the wheel. "In fact, Alec, *you* could be driving this car before we're done with it."

I spin the numbers in my head. I can get the learner's permit on my 15th birthday—December 31, 1956—if it's not a Saturday or Sunday. Then one year later—the license! And then I can take it out by myself—or maybe with Bonnybelle sitting close beside me. Oooh man! Wouldn't *that* be cool! I sit back, close my eyes and dream about a day that will never come.

Mom has scheduled dinner for six o'clock, so Dad and I drive over to Rockwood Hill at 5:30. Bonnybelle has arranged to spend the night with Mrs. Phillips, so we park by the store and I walk up to the house next to it and rap on the door. Mrs. Phillips ushers me into the front room and tells me to wait. "She'll be down in just a minute," she promises.

It's more like three minutes, and it seems like three hours.

Finally I hear footsteps on the stairs and Bonnybelle appears, flashes me a smile and curtseys. "Hope I done that right," she says. "Been a-practicin' fer ten minutes. How do I look?"

She looks absolutely beautiful, like someone completely transformed. Her party dress is pure white, and Mrs Phillips has fixed her hair with grey-green ribbons that match her eyes. Is this the same migrant girl with the dirty t-shirt and boy's jeans? Reading Shaw or seeing *My Fair Lady* is still a decade away, but Bonnybelle Wakely is a miniature blonde Eliza Doolittle, complete with freckles and—*Oh Jeez Loueeze!*

Mrs. Phillips reacts about the same time I do. "Oh dear! I'm afraid you've used a little too much perfume, Honey!"

A little too much? She smells like she's taken a bath in it!

Bonnybelle's chin quivers again. "I'm sorry, Miz Phillips!" she cries. "It just smelled so dang good I wanted to make sure Alec'd notice it!" Well, I notice it all right, and so will anyone else who gets within twenty feet of her.

"Don't fret now, Honey," Mrs. Phillips tells her. "It's nothing a little soap and water can't fix." She hauls Bonnybelle off to the bathroom and I hear the sound of running water. When they return, the smell is still noticeable, but it's a lot less potent.

"Now remember what I told you," Mrs. Phillips warns.

"Yes, Ma'am. I always say *please* an' *thank you*, an' I don't take seconds less'n they're offered to me."

"That should cover it," Mrs. Phillips says. "Now you have my number in case you need to call. Alec, I want her back here no later than 8:30."

"Yes, Mrs. Phillips," I agree.

"I hope yer mama offers seconds," Bonnybelle confides as we head out the door. "I skipped lunch so's I'd have room fer lots—oh My Lord!" She catches sight of our new Pontiac. "Alec, I didn't know you was rich folks!"

"We're not really. This is the first new car we've ever had, and Dad just got it today. You'll be the first person outside the family to ride in it."

"An' I'm a-gonna stink it up with this dern ol' perfume!"

Bonnybelle looks ready to cry again, so I quickly open the door and practically push her inside.

"Bonnybelle, this is my dad," I say as I climb in after her. "Dad, this is Bonnybelle Wakely."

Give Dad credit. The smell doesn't faze him. "I'm very pleased to meet you, Bonnybelle," he says as he starts the engine. His nose twitches once, but he doesn't jangle his ring of keys at all.

Well, here I am in the back seat of a Pontiac with a girl for the second time this year. Different Pontiac and different girl, but the same nervous, tingling feeling runs through me. We cruise slowly down Rockwood Hill, across the Star Mill and past the park to our house on Fifth and Adams. Just as with Mary Alice, I keep a couple of feet between Bonnybelle and me, but she makes no objection when I take her hand and hold it.

The smell doesn't faze Mom either, but Bonnybelle's beautiful white party dress does. She tells us that dinner will be ready in ten minutes, so why don't I show her the house in the meantime? But as we leave, she says, "Just a minute, Alec," and beckons me back into the kitchen.

"That poor girl is going to spill gravy or butter or ice cream all over that beautiful outfit," she says. "I can tell she's not used to wearing anything so fancy, but I don't want to embarrass her. So here's what we'll do..."

I take Bonnybelle on a quick tour through the house, show her my room and point out my three most prized posessions: the Nieuport 17, my comic book collection and the baseball Red Adams signs for me. Bonnybelle just shakes her head.

"Alec, yuh got a whole room to yerself!" she says wonderingly. "I ain't never even had muh own bed!"

"But you will," I tell her. "And soon. Your dad has a good job now, and you told me he's saving his money. You'll be out of that old trailer in no time."

Bonnybelle's chin quivers again. "I'm a-tryin' so hard to

believe it," she says, "but I keep a-havin' bad dreams at night. It's like somethin' terrible's a-gonna happen, an' there's nothin' I kin do to stop it!" She starts shaking, and I want to call Mom for help. But I get her into this by showing her the room, so it's my job to get her out again. I put my arms around her and rock her gently like Mrs. Phillips does until the shaking stops and her old happy-go-lucky face slips back into place.

"Sorry I'm bein' such a sissypants," she says. "Hey! Yuh got any of Jimmy Wakely's comics in that there stack?"

"No, but I know where I can get you one." Pete Guiness has one he'd like to get rid of, but if he senses I want it, he'll hold out for my newest *Blackhawk* in trade. What the heck— I'll do it. Trading a new *Blackhawk* for an old *Jimmy Wakely*— I guess that means I'm in love.

"Dinner's ready, you two!" Mom calls, and we scramble back downstairs. Mom has set the fancier dining room table instead of the old one in the kitchen, and she's put on a white tablecloth. "Hold it, Alec!" she says as we start to seat ourselves. She gives me a wink and I get set to play my part.

"That's Alec's best shirt," she explains to Bonnybelle, "and he is probably the clumsiest eater on earth. So I'm getting out—".

"Aw, Mom! Not that!" I say and try to sound convincing as she takes a huge double-size napkin from a drawer and ties it around my neck like a bib.

"Do you know how hard I had to work to get the stains out last time?" she recites. "Oh, Bonnybelle, I hate to impose on you, but Alec would feel a lot less embarrassed if you wore one too. And it would protect that beautiful dress," she adds as an afterthought.

"Reckon I wouldn't mind none, Ma'am," Bonnybelle says, and even I can see the relief in her face. Sometimes I think Mom belongs in the diplomatic corps.

Since this is a special dinner, we say grace before we dig in. Mom has cut up and cooked two whole chickens, so there are eighteen pieces to serve out. Bonnybelle and I go through four apiece, along with an ear of corn each and a double helping of mashed potatoes and gravy for her and a single for me. For the first five minutes she eats like a machine. Then, when she realizes it isn't all going to vanish, she loosens up and begins to talk.

"This is the bestest dinner I ever had in all muh life, Miz Lewis! Reckon I've just 'bout died an' gone to heaven!"

"Well, it's good to see someone enjoying her dinner," Mom says. "Alec just picks at his food sometimes." (This is unfair, since I've been matching Bonnybelle bite for bite.) "Now save a little room for dessert. We have ice cream with chocolate or butterscotch topping—or both, if you would like."

"Lordy! Do yuh eat like this ever' day?"

"Oh no!" Mom laughs. "We'd all weigh 400 pounds apiece if we did. This is a special day because you're here with us." Count on Mom to know the right thing to say and the right time to say it.

"Man, I sure wish muh daddy coulda had some of this. He just loves fried chicken, but Mama ain't got no place to fix it fer him."

"Then why don't I wrap up two or three pieces for you to take back to him?"

"Yuh'd do that fer me?"

"Of course. He must really be special for you to think of him like that."

"Reckon he is, Miz Lewis. Reckon he just 'bout saved muh life this past summer."

"Really?"

"Yes, Ma'am. It was 'bout a month after muh brother Jesse drowned. I was a-walkin' back from the camp store. Usually I'd go with Jesse, but he was dead an' gone, so I hadta go it alone. It was gettin' close to dark, and I was almost back when these three men done grabbed me."

"Mercy!" Mom says.

"They was drunk. I could smell it, and I reckon they figgered to haul me off inta the brush and do me over. One of 'em had his hand over muh mouth, but I got muh teeth 'round his thumb and chomped him till he yelled and let go, and then I started hollerin' till Daddy heard me, an' he come a-runnin'."

"What did he do?" I ask.

"You shoulda seen him, Alec. He had his ol' barlow knife out and he stuck one of 'em right in the gizzard! Then he slashed another up so bad he dang near bled to death. The third one still had hold of me, but I'd wrapped muh teeth 'round his thumb again, an' I was a-doin' muh best to chaw it off. But when Daddy started fer him, he clouted me on the side of muh head to make me turn loose, and then he took off fer the hills 'bout as fast as he could go. I saw stars fer five minutes, but that's 'bout all the harm I come to, thanks to Daddy!"

"Merciful heaven!" Mom exclaims. "Did those terrible men go to prison?"

"No, Ma'am. The law don't bother much with folk like us. A depity came out an' talked to me some. Then he said there warn't nothin' he could do 'cause they hadn't ackshully done nothin' to me. He said he figgered Daddy an' me'd fixed 'em a lot worse'n the law could. Do yuh suppose I could have just a bit more of them smashed taters an' gravy, please?"

By the time we finish with the ice cream (both toppings for Bonnybelle, chocolate for me), it's after seven. Bonnybelle's bib has collected several big splotches, so I deliberately dribble a little chocolate on mine. "I'd be pleased to help yuh with the dishes, Ma'am," she says as we stand up from the table.

"Heavens, Bonnybelle! You're our guest. Henry and I can take care of the dishes. Wait! Both of you wash your hands before you touch anything. There's grease from that chicken all over them. Alec's favorite program will be on in a few minutes. Have you every listened to *The Whistler,* Bonnybelle?"

"Don't reckon I have, Ma'am."

"Then why don't you do that while we do the dishes. Then I'm afraid it will be time to take you back."

I turn off the overhead light, set the Philco's dial to KOIN and then switch off the lamp by the couch where we're sitting. "More fun to listen to this in the dark," I explain. After a commercial the whistling begins. *S-i-g-n-a-l. Signal! Signal Gas-o-line!* Then Bill Forman's voice takes over. *"I am The Whistler, and I know many things, for I walk by night..."*

Bonnybelle grabs hold of my hand and whispers, "Oh man! This is one of them scary programs, ain't it?"

"Not all that scary—usually," I reassure her (although with *The Whistler* you never can be sure). "If it was really bad, my folks wouldn't let me listen to it."

Well, this episode is pretty tense, a modern variation of *Hansel and Gretel,* about a scheming woman who marries and then murders a wealthy widower to get his money. But she discovers that he's left it all in a trust for his two children, Henry and Greta (coincidence? I don't think so.), so she has to get rid of them as well. The plot centers on her schemes to arrange "accidents" for them, all the while pretending to be the loving and doting stepmom. By the commercial break, Bonnybelle is shivering.

"Look," I tell her. "We don't have to listen to this if you don't want to."

"No. I kin stand it if'n yuh kin. But I'd be mighty obliged if'n yuh'd put an arm 'round me."

I do and she cuddles against me while the story plays out. I'm thinking, *what's with her? Here's a girl who can walk on her hands, and nearly bites the thumb off a grown man when he attacks her. Yet she's scared silly by a radio program. Why?*

The episode ends with the wicked stepmother being snared in one of her own traps, and Henry and Greta going to live with a set of doting grandparents. Bonnybelle gives me a hug when I turn the lamp back on. "That was fun, Alec! I like a good scare when I got someone to hold onto."

So is that why she likes to go ripping down Rockwood Hill on the back of my bike? She won't do it by herself, even when I offer the old Columbia to her, yet she trusts me to take her through the turn safely. Well, it does feel good to hold her, expecially in the dark. I don't try to get fresh, though, since I'd like to keep my thumbs intact. I get the feeling that in a fight she would probably clean my clock, and that you don't mess with her unless she wants you to.

Bonnybelle spends the ride back to Mrs. Phillips' house telling Dad how wonderful we all are and that she's never had such a good time in all her life. Yeah, I hear people say things like that all the time, but there's something in the way she says it that tells me she means every word. And yet she's not gullible.

All that stuff 'bout the napkin," she says to me with a sly smile. "You wore that just so's I wouldn't feel like a baby ner mess up muh new dress, right? And yuh meant to dribble that chocolate on it, didn't yuh?"

"Well..."

"Mr. Lewis, ain't he 'bout the wonderfullest boy in the world?"

That sets Dad to jangling his keys again. "Well, *sometimes* he can be that way," he finally admits.

"Reckon he is, an' I sure hope I get to marry him someday!" she says with a note of determination that makes me a little nervous.

"That could be something to look forward to, but let's wait until you both grow up," Dad says as we pull up in front of Mrs. Phillips'. "You have years and years before you have to make that kind of decision."

Bonnybelle's face turns suddenly sad as she gets out. "Mr. Lewis, Sir, it's kind of you to say that. But somehow I don't reckon I do."

I'm trying to puzzle out what she means by that as I walk her up to the door. There are things about Bonnybelle that I don't understand and perhaps never will. I tell her goodnight and thanks for coming over and wait for another peck on the cheek, but instead she turns her face to me and says, "Lips is all right now, and yer daddy's bein' a gent an' lookin' the other way."

Well, compared to what kids can see in the movies or on television today, it's really not much of a kiss, but it's like nothing I ever experience before. Mary Alice kisses me too, but I always feel she does it out of a sense of duty—like she owes me something and is paying off a debt. With Bonnybelle I get a feeling of the sheer simple joy of being alive. I can't explain it, can't define it, but it's there.

"G'night," she says as she slips inside. Just as the door closes she adds, "Reckon I just 'bout love yuh, Alec Lewis!" Then she's gone and I'm walking back to the car.

"From Mary Alice Patterson to Bonnybelle Wakely," Dad says as we drive home. "Son, you sure do know how to hit the extremes."

"How do you describe her, Dad? There's something about her—but I don't know what it is."

"There is, to be sure." Dad thinks about it as we head back across the Star Mill. He's a meticulous man, as careful with his words as he is with numbers. "I can think of just one word to describe her. *Fey*."

"What does that mean?"

"You can look it up when we get home. It has several meanings. Some are good and some aren't. For her sake and yours, I hope it's the good that apply."

I do look it up just before I go to bed. There are four different meanings, and I like two of them. One is, *having visionary power,* and a second is *enchanted or under a spell.* But the other two prickle the hair on the back of my neck—*fated to die soon* and *full of the sense of approaching death.* Man, I hope Dad and the dictionary are wrong on that!

****

On Saturday the 26th, Dad drives me over to Lofgrens so that Bonnybelle can return the favor. Mom won't let me skip lunch, but I eat as little as possible so I'll be ready for whatever they put in front of me. It turns out to be a mulligan stew, and when I ask Mr. Lofgren how it's made, he just laughs.

"It's an old hobo dish we used to make back in the 20's and 30's when I was ridin' the rails," he explains. "Whatever you could beg, borrow or steal—thrown into a big old pot and cooked over a campfire by the tracks. Nowadays Clara makes me buy the stuff at the store and she cooks it on the stove, so it don't taste quite as good. But I reckon it'll do."

"And I helped to mix an' cook it too," Bonnybelle adds. "Spent most a whole hour a-stirrin' so's it'd be just right." She grins at me and adds, "So yuh'd better eat ever' little bit I set in fronta yuh, *Mr.* Alec Lewis!"

I do. Two helpings, in fact. It's really pretty good. Just as I'm finishing up, there's a timid knock at the door, and Bonnybelle's mom and dad come in.

"You 'bout finished eatin'?" Mr. Wakely asks.

"Perfect timing, Ray," Mr. Lofgren answers. "We've got plenty left over, if'n you'd like a bite."

"We'll take some back fer Roger. He's mindin' John Henry fer us. Muh daughter says that you folks an' young Lewis here might like to hear some playin' an' singin'."

Ray Wakely takes a seat on the living room couch and pulls an old Gibson guitar from a battered case as the rest of us troop in to join him. Bonnybelle throws herself down by her dad as he puts the instrument in tune. He strums a couple of chords, twists a peg and, apparently satisfied, asks her, "What do yuh reckon they'd like to hear?"

"Let's do *Billy the Kid* first. Play it in E, Daddy. You lead off and I'll come in."

Ray Wakely does the first two lines solo in his low baritone. Then on the third line Bonnybelle's voice comes in, high and pure as a mountain stream.

"Way out in New Mexico, long, long ago..."

The blend of her voice with his creates an effect that probably can't be duplicated on a recording, but it sends a shiver down my back. After *Billy the Kid,* they do another duet. Then Bonnybelle begs her mother to join in.

"Oh, Honey!" she protests. "I ain't sung in fronta folks since way before John Henry was born. You two do the singin' an' I'll just listen."

"Please, Mama! I wanta do *Bandit Queen of the Badlands* fer Alec, an' it don't sound right less'n you do the high harmony."

Mrs. Wakely finally shakes her head and sighs. "Oh, all right, Honey. Just this once, fer you. But I'm prob'ly gonna sound like an ol' screech owl."

"No you won't, Mama! Play it in C, Daddy. I'll do the lead. I know all the verses."

Bonnybelle sings the first verse solo. Then, on the chorus, her mother and father come in. For a couple of bars they seem to grope. Then, suddenly, the three voices mesh like a transmission slipping into gear, and the effect is chilling.

"Belle Starr! Belle Starr! You may wander near and far,
But the pale horse runs behind you, and you can't outride your past.
Wander east, wander west, 'cross this land you love the best.
That ol' pale rider will catch up to you at last."

I'm so caught up in the song that I don't even notice the knock at the door. Neither do the Wakelys. But as the song ends, I hear someone say, "Holy Toledo!" and when I turn, Dad is standing there in the doorway.

"That's fantastic!" he adds as he comes in. "I've never heard that one before."

"That's 'cause Daddy wrote it all by hisself, Mr. Lewis. Wrote it just fer me, too."

"Sing the chorus one more time, will you?" Dad asks, and they do. "I would dearly love to have a recording of that," he says. "Is there another where you all sing together?"

Ray Wakely shakes his head, but Bonnybelle blurts out, "Daddy! I bet we could still do *Will the Circle Be Unbroken?* Would yuh like to hear that one, Mr. Lewis?"

"Well, Alec has to get up at five tomorrow morning to do his route, so I have to get him home pretty soon. But if it's one where the three of you sing together—I think we could stay a few minutes longer."

The Wakelys take that old gospel standard and once again weave their magic on it. As Bonnybelle's mother's voice grows stronger and more assured, the lines seem to fade from her face and for a few minutes she becomes a beautiful woman again. Mr. Wakely's low baritone rumbles like an organ, and Bonnybelle herself sings the melody with a simple grace that cements everything together.

"You were right," Dad comments as we drive home. "There definitely is something about her, about that whole family. But Son, I have this feeling that Bonnybelle is going to break your heart."

"Dad, she told me the other night she just about loves me."

"I'll bet she did and I'll bet she does, but I can sense trouble ahead. I don't know what it is or where it is, but it's out there."

Well if it is, I can't see it. September is a golden month. The skies cloud over sometimes, but the rain holds off, and every weekday Bonnybelle runs beside me from Lofgren's over to Mrs. Phillips'. Then she hops on the carrier stand and we rip down Rockwood Hill together. September of 1953 turns out to be just about the best month of my life, and I'm glad.

Because October is the worst.

Chapter Fourteen: The Dreams

On the first of October I have to start collecting again. By the time I reach Rockwood Hill it's getting close to five, and I'm going to have to hurry to finish on time. Bonnybelle is waiting on Mr. Lofgren's porch and runs beside me as I finish the deliveries. Cap'n Andy appears and I let her give him a Wednesday edition.

"Thanka, Bobble. You nice," he says, and Bonnybelle gives him what would be a pretty good curtsey if she wears a dress instead of jeans.

"Yer right welcome, Mr. Slade." She says it with no trace of irony, which is good because Cap'n Andy can tell when he's being teased, and it doesn't take much to set him off.

I buy a big blue jawbreaker for each of us when I stop to collect from Mrs. Phillips. Bonnybelle pops hers in her mouth and grins. "Won't be long now afore the school duds is paid off, an' then I'll be a-buyin' 'em fer yuh," she says. At least I think that's what she says. It's kind of hard to talk clearly while sucking on a jawbreaker close to the size of a ping-pong ball.

I let her get three of the last five houses while I stop to collect from the other two. "It's late, but I guess we got time for one quick ride down the hill, if you want," I say as I pop my jawbreaker in my cheek and suck on it. She says nothing

—just hops on the carrier stand, wraps her arms around my waist and jams the side of her head between my shoulder blades. She gives just one little squeal as we fly into the turn, but she's hugging me hard enough to squeeze me in two.

"Hey Alec," she says as we coast to a stop and start back across the Star Mill. "Couldja do somethin' fer me?"

"Sure, I guess. What?"

"Couldja take me along on yer whole route, come Saturday? I'd kinda like to see all of it."

"It's a long one, and you don't have a bike," I warn her. "It starts clear over on the other side of the tracks."

"Won't bother me none. I kin run a mile, if'n I hafta."

"All right then. Be at Mrs. Phillips' a little after ten. I'll pick you up there."

"Great!" she says. We reach the foot of the old white bridge and she hops off and kisses me right on the mouth. A couple of teenagers driving out Western Avenue see us and whistle, and I can feel my face go red.

"I wish you wouldn't do that right out here in front of everybody," I tell her.

"Shoot! Bet it's nothin' *they* ain't already done! If them two's old enough to go drivin' together, they're old enough to park 'n spark. Bet we could take lessons from 'em." Then she relents. "But I won't, if'n it's gonna make yuh go all red like that."

So instead of kissing me again, she takes her jawbreaker out of her mouth and says, "Gimme yours." I hand it over and she pops it in her mouth and says, "Reckon I loves yuh germs an' spit an' all, Alec Lewis, and I'm wonderin' if'n yuh love me too."

There's only one answer I can make. I take her jawbreaker, stick it in my mouth and suck on it. "Germs and spit and all, Bonnybelle," I say to her.

****

"Alec, there's a letter for you," Mom informs me when I come in from my route Friday afternoon. I assume it's from Mary Alice, but Mom says no. "It's from clear back east," she says. "I'll bet it's that author you wrote to last summer."

I tear it open and begin to read.

Dear Mr. Lewis,

I am sorry to be so late responding to your letter, but deadline pressures, two short stories plus a technical article on aviation, have kept me fairly busy. However, I think I may have come across some information that may be of use to you.

There is no combat record for a Quentin Patterson in the files of the Lafayette Escadrille. However, there is a notation that a Corporal Q. L. Patterson was killed in 1917 when his plane stalled during takeoff. This apparently occurred on his second or third patrol.

Stalling an engine on takeoff was quite common among inexperienced pilots, and even some of the veterans met their fate in this manner. Major James McCudden, the British ace, was killed in this manner in 1918. Stalling was usually caused by taking off at too steep an angle or banking too sharply. The Sopwith Camel was particularly notorious for this. The Nieuport 17 was easier to handle, but it too could be tricky. It is sad but interesting to note that in the First World War more pilots were killed in accidents than died in combat.

I will leave it to you as to whether you should share this information with your friend. As with sleeping dogs, it is sometimes best to let dead pilots lie in peace. If your friend's uncle is a hero in her eyes, why not let him remain that way?

Yrs. very sincerely,
Arch Whitehouse

So it's all a lie. Mary Alice's uncle dies from his own carelessness, and not from enemy bullets. He doesn't fall from the sky like a meteor. He pancakes onto his own airfield, and Mary Alice's grandfather probably knows it all along. He turns his son Bud into a bigot and forces his granddaughter to humiliate herself in front of her class every year—and it's all to protect a fraud and a sham.

But if he doesn't, Mary Alice wouldn't have to recite *In Flanders Fields* every year—which means I wouldn't decide to help her, wouldn't go up to her house for cookies, wouldn't nearly crash into Pat Rush, wouldn't become an *Oregon Journal* carrier and thus wouldn't meet Bonnybelle Wakely.

I decide I'm not going to tell Mary Alice anything about this.

****

Bonnybelle is strangely silent and somber when I stop by Mrs. Phillips' for her on Saturday morning. She gives me the barest ghost of a smile, sits back on the carrier stand with one hand holding me by the belt, and doesn't make a sound when I take the bike down the hill and through the turn onto the Star Mill, even though I go fast enough to make it all the way up to Second and Adams with her on the back. Finally she hops off and walks beside me.

"Okay, what's wrong?" I ask.

She doesn't answer for nearly half a block. Finally she says, "Alec, do yuh ever have dreams?"

"Yeah. Just about every night, I think."

"But do yuh ever have the same one over an' over?"

"Not really. There was this movie I saw back when I was in first or second grade that scared the blue willies out of me. I think it was called *The Enchanted Valley*, and it had a scene of a cougar stalking some kids. That gave me nightmares for three or four nights straight. Is that what you're talking about?"

"Naw. Mine ain't like that. I don't have it ever' night, and there ain't no monsters ner boogermen after me. But it's happened a buncha times in the last few weeks, an' it's really a-startin' to scare me."

"Well, what's it like?"

"Kinda hard to describe," she says as we walk the bike across Baker Street. "It's like I'm in this here room. Don't know where it is ner how I got there, but it's all white, and there ain't nothin' in it 'cept a big ol' calendar stuck up on the wall. Fer some reason I cain't make out the print, so I don't know if'n it's fer a day or a week or a month or a year. But the pitcher above the writin' is the purtiest thing I ever seen."

"So what happens?"

"I flip up the page, and the next one's got a pitcher that's even purtier, but I still cain't read the date. So I keep on a-flippin' and the pitchers keep a-getting' purtier. Then, all of a sudden, they stop."

"What do you mean?"

"I flip up a page an' the next one's blank—no pitcher, no writin', nothin! I keep on a-flippin' an' they all come up blank. So I try to go back, and now they're all blank too. Then I look again and the whole thing's gone, an' I'm just alone. Then I hear John Henry cryin' 'cause I'm a-cryin' an' kickin' him in muh sleep. So I wake up."

"Sheesh! How long has this been going on?"

"Ever since we moved up onta Rockwood Hill. First it was maybe once a week, but now it's ever' two or three days. That dream scares me, Alec. I dunno why, but it scares me awful bad!"

"Maybe it'll go away when you move out of that trailer and off Rockwood Hill."

"Oh man! I wanta move so bad! An' yet, I don't, Alec. I mean, Miz Phillips is there, an' she's just like a grandma to me. I ain't never had no grandma that I kin remember. An' Mr. and Miz Lofgren too—they've been real nice to me. An' you come up there 'most ever' day too. Oh Lordy, Alec! I'm scared to go an' I'm scared to stay! What am I a-gonna do?"

Please, Bonnybelle! I think. *Don't go all shaky on me! Not here!* She doesn't, but it's close. I have her by the arms, and I can feel a big shudder ripple through her. Then she's back in control of herself once more.

"Dang! I'm bein' a sissypants again! Yuh must think I'm crazy or somethin'."

"I don't think you're crazy, Bonnybelle, but something sure is scaring you. And I know you don't scare easy."

"I ain't much scared of anythin' I kin see. It's the things I just pitcher in muh head, like that *Whistler* program or these here dreams—things that ain't here, an' yet they are. Do yuh know what I mean? I ain't doin' a very good job of 'splainin' it."

"I think I get what you mean. Can I ask you something?"

"Sure. Go ahead."

"Do you keep your eyes closed when we go down the hill together?"

She finally grins. "Yeah. A little bitty scare's kinda fun once in a while. Hey! Hop on yer bike and let me run alongside yuh fer a coupla blocks. That allus makes me feel better."

She runs beside me all the way up to Galloway Street and then north for a block to Third. The *Journal* truck pulls in just as we get to Benny's, so we wait in the front while J. P. cuts the bundles and sets out the stacks for the carriers. Archer, Ferraday, Dixon and Rush are there early. The rest of the crew will drift in over the next hour or so. J. P. wants the Saturday papers delivered by three, which means nobody has to start much before one. But I like to start early, take my time and go home for lunch before doing Rockwood Hill.

Bonnybelle looks at the rows of bikes for sale and whistles. "Man! Daddy said he maybe might be able to get me one fer Christmas, if'n things work out right. How much do yuh reckon they cost?"

"Better ask Mrs.Benson," I tell her, and she does.

"We have used bicycles from under ten dollars and new ones all the way up to over a hundred," Mrs.Benson tells her. "What kind would you like to look at?"

"Don't reckon I could afford even one of the cheap ones now, Ma'am. But muh daddy might be fixin' to get me one later on."

"Well, we're not going to run out. You know, I don't believe I've seen you in here before, Honey. What's your name?"

"Muh name's Bonnybelle, an' I'm proud to meet yuh, Ma'am," she says very politely. Then she adds, "I'm Alec's girlfriend," and my heart drops down to my socks. Jill overhears her, gives me a wicked grin and races back to the *Journal* room to spread the news. Well, if I have to face it, it might as well be sooner than later.

"You wait out here while I get the papers ready," I tell her. "No girls allowed back in the *Journal* room."

"Oh? Whattyuh call that li'l thing what just ran back there?"

"That's Jill, and her dad owns the place. She can go anywhere."

"Yer all red again, Alec. Sorry if'n I opened muh big mouth. I'll wait out here if'n it'll make yuh feel better."

I march back to the *Journal* room, and for a few seconds nobody says a word. Then Jill slips out and Archer mutters, "Hey Lewis. You know the difference between a girl and a dartboard?"

"Not now, Dave. I feel bad enough already."

"Why?" J. P. asks. "Because a pretty young lady cares for you? Why don't you invite her back here to meet us?"

Huh? Five mouths drop open and ten eyes stare at J. P. as if he is suggesting that we all take the day off. Even Jill, hovering near the door, looks astonished.

"Of course," J. P. says as he takes out his pouch of Prince Albert and begins to stuff his pipe. "I would certainly like to meet the girl who could capture your attention. She must be very special."

I don't know if J. P. is sincere or if he's setting me up for something, but if the boss makes a suggestion, it's a good idea to follow it. "Bonnybelle!" I call to her. "Come on back. J. P. says it's okay."

"So," J. P. says as he jams the pipe in his mouth and takes out another kitchen match. "You are Alec's friend, huh? Do you help him with his route?"

"Sometimes he lets me get a few houses while he stops to collect, Mr. Harrington, Sir."

"Very practical of him," J. P. comments as he again lights the match with his thumbnail and draws the flame down into the bowl. "And does he pay you anything for this valuable service?"

"Well, he gets me a jawbreaker sometimes."

"Do you know how to fold the papers?" J. P. asks as he blows a cloud of Prince Albert smoke up at the ceiling.

"Nosir. Alec's a-plannin' to show me, but he ain't got 'round to it yet."

"Well, this would be a good time for it. Wouldn't you say so, Alec?"

I still don't know if I'm being set up or not, but I pull a paper off my stack and show Bonnybelle the six steps to folding a triangle. "Crease here, crease here, fold, fold, flip and stuff." I do it once more and then say, "Okay, you try it."

After one or two attempts, Bonnybelle gets the hang of it and produces a good, tight triangle. Of course Saturday editions, the smallest of the week, are easy.

J. P. puffs another cloud of smoke at us and says, "You know, this reminds me a bit of a day back in January. I'm wondering if Alec is going to get a candy bar and have Jill and Bonnybelle race for a couple of pieces."

"Oh no you don't!" exclaims Jill, who is still in the doorway. "I'm not racing another girl! Not for all the candy on Mom's counter!"

"Poor Twerp!" Rush sighs. "You missed your chance. Alec's got a girlfriend now, and you'll never get a chance to fold his papers—or kiss him either."

"Double uck!" Jill snaps, and stomps back to the front.

"What's that all about?" Bonnybelle asks.

"It's kind of a long story," I say as I start folding papers with her. "We'll each do half a dozen more. Then we can load up and get cracking. There's something I want to show you." Mainly I want to get her out of here before J. P. leaves and the real teasing begins.

We put the 41 regular Saturdays, plus Mr. Lofgren's bulldog and a leftover Friday for Cap'n Andy, in my front bag and lug them out to my bike. Jill pretends not to notice us. I sling a paper onto the front porch of the house just across the Southern Pacific tracks, and then we start working our way back down Third. When we reach the Flying-A station at Third and Ford, Bonnybelle says, "Hey! Can we stop here fer a few minutes? Daddy's a-workin' here this mornin'."

Mr. O'Dell, who owns the station, is a tall, gray-haired man who walks with a limp and always carries a cane with a polished silver handle. When Bonnybelle introduces herself, he says, "So, you're Ray Wakely's girl, huh? Your daddy sure does like to talk about you. Want to go back and see him for a sec?"

We head back to the shop and find Bonnybelle's dad working on the engine of a three-year-old Buick. "Hey, Daddy!" she calls, and he straightens up and wipes his hands.

"Hey, muh Bonny Girl! What are yuh doin' way down here?"

"Helpin' Alec with his route. Now don't yuh go playin' with muh hair!" she begs as he grabs her in a bear hug. "Miz Phillips just washed it fer me last night, an' yer hands is still all greasy."

"Oh my!" Ray Wakely groans. "Muy Bonny Girl's gettin' to be quite a lady. Next thing yuh know, she'll be wantin' lipstick an' makeup."

"Oh Daddy! Yuh know I hate them things!"

"Not fer much longer, I'll bet!" he says as he gives her one last squeeze and releases her. "When yuh get home, tell Mama I'll be back afore three."

I get a sudden inspiration and ask, "Mr. Wakely, can Bonnybelle stop for lunch at my place? We'll still finish the route by one."

"Is it okay with yer mama, Alec?"

"I'll call her from Dad's office. It's just a couple blocks from here. He's working this morning too."

"Well, if'n it's all right with yer mama, Alec, it's all right with me. But I don't want yuh puttin' her out none."

"We won't. I promise." Mr. Wakely nods and goes back to work on the Buick while we run back to my bike. Mr. O'Dell is waiting for us there.

"You know something, Miss Wakely?" he says very solemnly. "Your dad is just about the finest natural mechanic I've ever seen. He doesn't have any formal training, but he can look at or listen to an engine or a transmission, tell you what's wrong and fix it just like that." He snaps his fingers for emphasis. "Don't tell him I said this, but I plan to give him a raise next month and a nice bonus come Christmas—enough for him to get some things for a certain little girl he loves."

"Thank yuh kindly, Mr. O'Dell. I promise yuh I won't say a word." She puts on a smile for Mr. O'Dell, but as soon as we leave, she shakes her head.

"That's like another purty pitcher, Alec. I'm a-startin' to get scared again."

"Don't start thinking good things have to turn bad. Come on and help me."

She follows me through the barber shop and the Yamhill Hotel and then across Everett to Mom Jenkins' popcorn wagon. "Want to share a popcorn ball?" I ask.

"Don't reckon I ever had one."

"Then it's time you did." I give Mom Jenkins a dime and she hands me a big red one wrapped in waxed paper. "You can hold it," I tell Bonnybelle. "I can't get my hands sticky. Just let me have every other bite."

We hit a few more stores and race each other up sets of stairs to get the apartments, but at the Blue Moon I tell her to wait by the bike while I go in alone.

"Do yuh mean yuh get to walk right inta a saloon all by yerself?" she asks.

"Just to deliver the paper, but I can't take you in with me."

"Are yuh kiddin'! Daddy'd tan muh bee-hind somethin' fierce if'n I took one step in there!"

By the time I come back out, the popcorn ball is gone. I only get three bites.

Timmons & Lewis, Certified Public Accountants is located on the second floor of an old building on Third and Cowls, directly above the City Water & Light Department. Dad is busy with a stack of forms and an adding machine when we come in, but he manages to give us a bleak smile and pushes the forms aside.

"I don't understand how some of these so-called businesses manage to stay afloat, the way they keep records—or rather, *don't* keep them. I'd guess you two are the first normal people I've dealt with all morning. It's good to see you again, Bonnybelle. Are you keeping Alec out of trouble?"

"Tryin' my darndest, Mr. Lewis, Sir."

"Dad, can I call home and ask Mom if Bonnybelle can stay to lunch?"

He nods and goes back to his work. I pick up the receiver, tell the operator, "Eight-oh-one, please," and wait for Mom to come on the line.

"Of course," she says. "But it's nothing fancy, just soup and a sandwich. Oh yes, and some chocolate cake left over from last night."

"Great! Thanks, Mom! See you in five or ten minutes."

"Oh, Bonnybelle," Dad says as we turn to go. "I talked to Jim Davis at KMRN the other day. He has a studio out there at the station, and he'd like you and your dad and mother to come out there sometime next weekend. He'd like to record your singing."

"Yuh mean he'd make a record of us?"

"No, it would just be a tape. But he said if it's good, he'd play it on the air. And I'm sure he knows some people in the record business. You know, you three are good enough to sing professionally."

"Do yuh really think so, Mr. Lewis?"

"I do indeed. There's something about the way your voices blend. I can't describe how it works, but I know quality when I hear it. And you are good enough to sing solo, Young Lady."

"I do thank yuh fer sayin' it, Mr. Lewis, but…"

"No buts about it. Your dad works at O'Dell's Flying-A, doesn't he? I'll tell Jim to stop by and see him next week. Alec, tell your mother I won't be back for lunch."

He picks up another sheet and sighs over it as we race back down the stairs.

I get the police station and the big house right across from it on Second Street. Then I tell Bonnybelle to hop on the carrier stand, and I head for home. Mom already has our places set at the kitchen table.

"It's not much," she apologizes. "Just tomato soup and a roast beef sandwich, plus milk and some chocolate cake. Bonnybelle, I hope your mother won't be angry with me for feeding you."

"Reckon she won't mind none, Ma'am. If'n I want somethin' fer lunch, I purty much hafta fix it muhself." She rips through the sandwich, and Mom gives her seconds on the soup. I also notice that her piece of cake is nearly twice as big as mine.

"Need help with the dishes, Ma'am?" she says as she downs the last of the milk and wipes the mustache off her upper lip.

"No," Mom laughs. "You two go on and finish Alec's route. I have all afternoon."

"Hey!" I tell Bonnybelle. "I said I have something for you, remember?"

I take her up to my room, pull a comic book off the stack and hand it to her. Pete Guiness holds out for my newest *Blackhawk* in trade, but I finally have a *Jimmy Wakely*. "Sorry it's not the new one," I tell her, "but they're kinda hard to find."

I guess, coming on top of what Dad and Mr. O'Dell tell her, this is just a little too much good news for one morning. Bonnybelle stares at the comic book and her chin starts quivering again. *Oh no!* I think as I see the tears welling up in her eyes. The next thing I know she's bawling out loud. Then I hear footsteps on the stairs, and Mom is demanding, "Alec Lewis! What have you said or done to that girl?"

"He ain't done nothin', Miz Lewis! Honest Injun! It's just...it's just..."

Mom folds Bonnybelle into her arms like Mrs. Phillips does and rocks her gently until the sobbing subsides. "Is this, um, a girl problem?" she asks diplomatically. "Something you'd just as soon Alec not hear you talk about?"

I quickly get up to leave, but Bonmnybelle blurts out, "Oh no, Ma'am! It ain't muh period. I know all about that. It's just—so many wonderful things've been a-happenin', and I'm a-gettin' scared that...that..."

"Bonnybelle!" I interrupt. "Tell Mom about your dreams. Everything you told me. She'll know what to do."

Bonnybelle and Mom sit on my bed and she tells her about the dreams of the calendar going blank and the things that have happened over the last few weeks. "It's like everythin' I ever wished for is all of a sudden comin' true, an' I'm so scared somethin' awful's a-gonna come along an' wreck it all. It's like the time when...when..." She breaks down and starts crying again.

"Go get me a warm wash cloth, Alec," Mom says. When I return with it, she gently wipes Bonnybelle's face and says, "There now. Do you want to tell me about it? Alec can leave if you want him to."

"No, Ma'am. It's all right. I usta dream 'bout Jesse. He's muh brother what drowned down in Californey last spring. I'd dream we was a-walkin' down the road together, just laughin'an' havin' a good time. Then I'd turn to look at somethin' alongside the road, and when I'd turn back, he was gone. No word or sign—just like he'd never been there."

Mom is silent for nearly a minute. Finally she says, "Here is what I think. You dreamed about your brother because you love him and you miss him. That's perfectly natural. And as for this other dream—well, you probably haven't had that many good things in your life so far. Am I right?"

"Reckon yuh are, Ma'am."

"So there's probably a part of you somewhere that feels you don't deserve any happiness. It's telling you that you're worthless. Do you understand that?"

"I guess maybe so."

"Well, let me tell you something. You *are* worth all these good things—and more! You're one of the most remarkable people I've ever met, and I've met quite a few in my day. I can see why Alec is so wild about you."

"Aw, Mom!" I protest.

"Hush, Alec! That's a compliment. Bonnybelle, don't worry about what may happen in the future. Just live each day as it comes, and I'll bet they'll all be good ones. And if something really bad *should* happen in your family—well, you can have another home right here."

"Thank yuh fer sayin' that, Ma'am. Miz Lofgren and Miz Phillips done told me the same thing."

"That's because they feel the same way we do. I think just about everybody would love you, Bonnybelle. There's no one out there you're afraid of, is there?"

"Well, I was kinda 'fraid of Cap'n Andy—Mr. Slade, that is. But Alec introduced me to him right an' proper, an' now he calls me Bobble, 'cause he cain't quite say muh name." This finally brings a quick smile. Then it vanishes and she says, "An then..." Her voice trails off.

"Who, Bonnybelle? Is there someone else out there who frightens you?"

"No one 'cept...Muh Uncle Roger sometimes."

"And why does he frighten you?"

"It's 'cause he ain't quite right in the head. But it ain't his fault!"

"What do you mean?"

"He was in the war, over in North Africa, an' he got wounded an' then captured by the Germans. They put him in a prison camp somewheres, an' he was there more'n two years. He don't talk about it none, but I guess some awful things happened there."

"Oh, that poor man! What does he do that scares you?"

"He has bad dreams too, Miz Lewis. He'll yell and scream in the night, an' when he wakes up, he's all confused, an' he thinks he's back there in that camp or someplace in North Africa where they had this big battle where he got hisself wounded. Then, when he comes to hisself, he's all 'shamed an' tells us he ain't good fer nothin' an' we just oughta leave him aside the road somewheres. But after he's full awake fer a while, he's just as nice as can be."

"Heavens!" Mom says. "The poor man should be in the Veteran's Hospital up in Portland. They can help him there."

"We know that, Miz Lewis, but they don't wanta take him 'cause we ain't got no reg'lar address here in Oregon yet. But we're a-gonna get one next month or maybe the one after that. Daddy's a-lookin' fer a place, an' now he's got steady work, they cain't treat us like trash no more."

"Bonnybelle, you were never trash to us, and you never will be."

"I know, Ma'am. Yuh treat me like a lady, and that's what I wanta be. But I allus end up cryin' like a li'l ol' sissypants when I try. Makes me feel awful 'shamed."

"Well don't be," Mom tells her. "It's perfectly all right to cry in front of your friends, and that's what we are. I'll have a word with Alec's dad about your uncle. He knows some people up in Portland—and he knows some people who have places for rent here in town too. Maybe we can speed things up a bit for you."

"That'd be most kind of yuh, Miz Lewis." Mom's offer seems to break up the mood that covers Bonnybelle like dark, wet clouds. "Hey, Alec! We'd better get that route of yers finished afore yuh get in trouble. Kin I put the comic in yer bag fer safe keepin'? I don't wanta get it all wrinkled." She shows it to Mom and says, "Alec got this fer me. We think Jimmy could be muh cousin or somethin'. Wouldn't that be neat?"

"Yes it would," Mom replies, "and maybe someday he'll be the one proud to claim you!"

****

Bonnybelle hops on the carrier stand and we ride the two blocks to the library. As we walk in with the paper, I ask her, That battle your uncle was wounded and captured in—was that Kasserine Pass?"

"Yeah! I think that's what I heard Daddy call it once. How'd yuh know that, Alec? Was yer daddy in the war over there too?"

"No. My dad wasn't in the war."

"Muh daddy warn't neither. He don't say nothin', but I think he's awful 'shamed of it. That's why we keep Uncle Roger with us—'cause he fought fer his country, and we're 'bout all he has left now. But how'd yuh know 'bout that battle if'n yer daddy warn't there?"

I answer her by walking over to a shelf and pulling out Ernie Pyle's *Here Is Your War*. "It's in here," I say. "I read about it this summer."

"Yuh read that all the way through? But that's a grown-up's book!"

"Well, I did. And this one and this one too." I pull out *Brave Men* and *Last Chapter*.

"Whew! Yer really somethin', Alec Lewis!" Bonnybelle says it with a note of wonder, and it really makes me feel good. After all the things she's done that amaze me, I finally get a chance to impress her.

"Ahem!" Mrs. Carruthers interrupts in her best librarian's tone. "I assume you're going to give me the paper, Alec. A gentleman over there would like to read it."

I hand it over and introduce Bonnybelle. Mrs. Carruthers smiles and asks me, "Are you bringing me another helper? Is this young lady interested in volunteering?"

"Me? I ain't never been in a library like this afore." She stares openmouthed at the sets of shelves. "I didn't even know there *was* this many books!"

That brings another smile. "Well, would you like a card so you can check some out? I'd be happy to make one for you. We'll just need your address and telephone number. Do you live here in town or out in the country?"

Bonnybelle hangs her head. "In town, Ma'am. But we don't got no reg'lar address ner phone yet."

That doesn't stop Mrs. Carruthers. "I'll tell you what we can do then," she says. "If Alec trusts you, you can check one out on his card."

"That's right kind of yuh, Ma'am, but I reckon I'll wait till I kin get muh own. I'm beholdin' enough to Alec already."

As we head back to my bike, Bonnybelle cocks her head to one side and asks, "Alec, what'd she mean 'bout bringin' her *another* helper?" This girl doesn't miss much.

"It's a long story, and I'm not sure you want to hear it," I warn her.

"Oh? Well, I'm double-dang-certain-fer-sure positive I *would* like to hear it, *Mr.* Alec Lewis!"

So, as we work our way down Second Street and across the Star Mill, I tell her all about Mary Alice—from the time I help her recite *In Flanders Fields* until her father moves the family to Denver. By the time I finish, we're walking the bike up Rockwood Hill.

"So I ain't the first girl yuh ever kissed, huh?"

"Actually, you're the third, but Sandy Evans was clear back when I was in kindergarten."

"Shoot! That don't count fer nothin'! I swum nekked in the river with boys when I was six." Then she grins and adds, "But I don't do that no more, so don't yuh go a-gettin' any ideas."

"You're not jealous then?"

"Jealous of some poor li'l ol' thing what's a thousand miles away? I feel right sorry fer her, Alec. *Her* daddy's sneaky-mean. My daddy usta get mean afore he stopped his drinkin', but he warn't ever sneaky 'bout it."

"When did he stop?"

"Right when Jesse drowned. It was a Sunday and we warn't workin'. Daddy'd passed out and warn't there to save him when the cramp got him. When he came to hisself, he poured it all out, an' he ain't touched a drop since. That's lucky fer me, 'cause he was right there when them three men tried to take me. Yuh know, that was on a Sunday too, an' I think Amy Rose died on a Sunday. Guess Sundays ain't been very lucky fer us."

Well, I get lucky with my collecting and catch a couple of holdouts at home, so I have plenty of money in my pocket when we reach Mrs. Phillips'. I offer to get Bonnybelle a candy bar this time, but she only wants a jawbreaker. "Get yerself one too," she says, and of course I know what she wants to do. We pop them in our mouths and walk outside, wait for a minute until they're good and sticky, then solemnly take them out and make the exchange.

"Reckon I loves yuh, Alec Lewis. Germ an' spit an' all."

"Germs and spit and all, Bonnybelle."

****

We finish the route and I ask her if she wants a ride back down the hill. "Naw," she says. "Not today. Come back with me to my place."

When we reach the trailer, there's no sign of her family. "Mama an' Uncle Roger must have John Henry over to Mr. Lofgren's to play. They got some old toys fer when their grandkids come down. But that's good, 'cause I wanta show yuh somethin."

She opens one of the two doors inside the trailer and shows me the room she shares with her little brother. It's hardly bigger than a closet, and there's no furniture—just a single mattress on the floor and a couple of cardboard boxes with clothes spilling out of them. Heck, there isn't room for anything else. Two blankets lie folded neatly on the mattress, and a single small window about head height looks out on Lofgren's neat back yard.

"Where's all the stuff Mrs. Phillips got for you?" I ask.

"We keep 'em over to her place. I get up in the mornin', put on Jesse's ol' jeans, and then run over to her house an' change fer school. Don't tell Mama ner Daddy, but Miz Phillips gets me breakfast too. Then Miz Taylor across the road drives me to school 'long with her two kids."

"So what did you want to show me?"

"This, Alec! This is all I've ever known. An' now we got a chance at somethin' so much better. Do yuh see why them dreams scare me so much? Lordy! If anythin' happened to me or John Henry, Mama an' Daddy'd just go all to pieces. They're barely hangin' on as is."

As we leave, I notice something strange about her door. It has *two* sliding bolt locks, one on the inside and one on the outside.

"Why two locks?" I ask her.

"Daddy put the first one up fer me, 'cause Uncle Roger walks in his sleep sometimes, an' he can be awful scary when he does. But that made him mad, so he put the second one up. He said if'n he cain't come in, then we cain't get out. But Daddy unlocks it after Uncle Roger goes to sleep, so's I can take John Henry to the bathroom. He still cain't make it through the night without peein' hisself."

Bonnybelle waits until I'm on my bike and ready to start for home before she says, "Alec, don't tell yer mama this, but I reckon she figured I had them dreams 'bout walkin' down the road with Jesse after he drowned. I didn't. I had 'em *afore* he drowned!"

Chapter Fifteen: Pale Rider

"*Alec Lewis has a new girlfriend.*"

You can't keep a secret in a small town. The rumor seeps out of Benny's, percolates down Third Street along my route and makes its way out to Cozine by Momday morning. Nobody says anything, but I can tell by the way my classmates—especially the girls—look at me that they've all heard about it.

"She goes to another school. She's not one of us."

I'm already considered something of an oddball, since I deliver papers after school instead of playing sports. No one at Cozine has ever carried the *Journal*. Unless it's pouring rain, I keep the bags on my bike when I ride it to school, just so everyone will know I'm proud of my job.

"Ever since school started, he's acted so strange. I wonder what she's like."

I act like I'm not aware of their stares, but I can see the questions in their eyes.

"Well, she has to be better than that stupid Little Miss Peepants. What happened to her, anyway? Someone said they all moved to Colorado."

"Well, I heard this new girl lives on Rockwood Hill and goes to Fox Glen!"

"Eeuuw! That's almost as bad as being an Okie!"

"Yeah! Can you imagine having an Okie for a boyfriend, Claudia?"

"Creepers! Are you trying to make me throw up? That's too disgusting to think about!"

"Do you think Alec would tell who she is if one of us asked him?"

"No. He might tell Janet, but she won't ask him."

"Yeah, what's with her, anyway? I thought she and Alec hated each other. Now they act like they're almost friends."

Well, we're not exactly friends, but the truce is holding. It has to, because we're now working together. Mr. Hunter and Mr. Jackson decide that Cozine should have a school newspaper, so they pick one student from each room as co-editors. Of course, they choose Janet and me.

I guess it's an honor, but I'm not sure if I want it. I try to tell Mr. Hunter that I can't stay very long after school, since I have papers to deliver. But he just says fine—Janet and I can work on it during noon recess. But after a couple of days spent mostly glaring at each other, we find that we make a pretty good team. I come up with a wild idea, and Janet shoots it full of holes. Then I patch it up and she says, "Okay, that *might* work." Then it's her turn to come up with an idea and my turn to shoot holes in it. Then we show the ideas to Mr. Hunter and Mr. Jackson and *they* shoot holes in them, but they're not nearly as critical as we are with each other.

****

October begins with the New York Yankees beating Brooklyn in the World Series, four games to two. Pat Rush and I are foolish enough to bet on the Dodgers, so Pietrowski collects a candy bar and pepsi from each of us. Portland ends its 180-game season at 92-88 and in fourth place in the PCL, the same spot as when I see them in June.

It's raining on Monday the 3rd so Bonnybelle waits for me at Mrs. Phillips'. "Hey!" she says. "Mr. Davis come out and talked to Daddy today, an' he wants him an' me an'

Mama to come out to the station Saturday night. Says he wants to interview all of us an' then have us sing a few song ballads—an' if they're good, he'll play 'em on the air. Whattyuh think of that, Alec?"

"I think it's fantastic."

"He wants us to sing fer the Rotary Club too—but Mama won't do that, 'cause she gets awful scared singin' in fronta people she don't know. But Daddy an' me kin do some duets. Could be the Rotary'll pay us some cash money fer singin' too!" The thought lights up Bonnybelle's face until it seems to glow.

"An' Daddy says I'm old enough now to learn to play his guitar!" she adds. "He's a-teachin' me at night, an' I'm a-pickin' it up purty good. But it sure makes muh fingers awful sore!"

****

And so we drift through Ocober. The country breathes a long sigh of relief that the war in Korea is finally over and the boys—most of them—are coming home. We avoid a war with Russia and China, and we don't lose this "police action." But we don't win either. It's a stalemate, and the United States is not used to ties.

Some of the returning soldiers, generally prisoners released by the reds, are not very happy with their country either. A sinister new word makes its way into our language—*brainwashed.*

(Mom and Dad tell me to watch for new words and phrases and record them in my journal. Some of the new ones they help me to find and record are *egghead, countdown, split-level, jet stream* and *cookout.*)

Things are happening in 1953. Sometimes we see them and sometimes we don't. An obscure case called *Brown v. Board of Education* is making it's way toward the Supreme Court, where it will be decided in 1954. The ruling will make racial segregation in America's public schools illegal. But it won't get rid of it.

Chevrolet brings out a sleek new sports car with a fiberglass body. They call it the Corvette, and it sells for $3250. Dad says it's too expensive and impractical and will never catch on. In December the *Journal* will front-page a story about a new midget electronic brain that is no bigger than a console television set and can easily be carried by two men. The company making it calls it a computer, and it sells for $7350. Dad wonders why anyone would want to spend that kind of money for a glorified adding machine.

After meeting Bonnybelle, I start taking an interest in music. Most of what we hear is pretty bland. Eddie Fisher tops the charts with *I'm Walking Behind You*. (Dirty Dave does a parody of this that's hilarious, but too off-color to be included here.) Other big hits are *Eh, Cumpari!, Rags to Riches, Vaya Con Dios* and *How Much Is That Doggie in the Window?* But things are changing here too.

In the fall of 1953 a young man walks into Sam Phillips' studio in Memphis and asks to make a record as a present for his mother. The young man's name is Elvis Presley. Negro stations in the East and South feature a new kind of music called rhythm and blues, and white kids start to listen and like what they hear. In Cleveland a white disc jockey named Alan Freed coins a new phrase to describe a certain type of rhythm and blues. He calls it rock 'n roll.

But I have a more important problem to ponder. Pietrowski is quitting, and J. P. asks me if I would like to move up to his route. Pete has eight more customers, so I would make almost four dollars extra each month. But it would mean saying goodbye to all the people along Third, to Mrs. Carruthers, the Lofgrens, Mrs. Phillips—and Bonnybelle.

Of course, Bonnybelle's family will be moving soon too—but where? Probably not onto Pete's route, but can I be sure of that? I agonize over the problem and finally decide to keep Route Three. A new guy by the name of Mike Freeman will take over Pete's route, but I'm still the baby of the bunch. Mike is a full year older than I am.

Dad is not pleased with my decision to stay put. "Eight more customers comes out to more than forty extra dollars in a year that you are throwing away," he tells me. "Bonnybelle's family will only be up on Rockwood Hill for a few more weeks. Then they'll be moving."

"I know, Dad. But there are apartments on my route. Maybe they'll move into one of them."

"And maybe they won't. There are places for rent all over town. Look, Alec, even if she's not on your route, it's not like she's moving to Denver. You'll still be able to see her."

Ouch! That little dig hurt. In June I am certain that Mary Alice Patterson is the great love of my life and that I will never get over losing her. Now I hardly think of her unless she sends me a letter, and I have to force myself to write back and try to sound like I'm glad to hear from her. Understanding the mystery of love is awfully hard when you're not quite twelve. Mom assures me that it doesn't get any easier as you get older.

****

On Wednesday the 5th we get our school pictures back, and mine turn out pretty doggone good. Mom and Dad like them too and order a full set—an eight by ten for themselves, five by sevens for Grandma Lewis and Grandma and Grandpa Fullerton. A sheet with miniatures of everyone in Mr. Hunter's room and a dozen more miniatures for me to swap with friends.

Bonnybelle has hers taken too, and Mrs. Phillips insists on buying her full set. "We'll keep it quiet," she says when I deliver her paper on Thursday. "I'll pick up a frame, Honey, and you can surprise your Mama and Daddy with the big one for Christmas. Of course I want one of the smaller ones to put with my other grandbabies, and I suppose Alec just *might* be willing to swap a miniature with you."

Her pictures actually come out better than mine. Bonnybelle has the kind of face that looks even better in two dimensions than it does in three. The photographer has her turn just slightly to the right to catch the little tilt to her nose, highlight the spatter of freckles across one cheek and show the ribbon in her hair. She wears that blouse with the lace collar that she modeled for me a month ago.

I borrow a pencil from Mrs. Phillips and write *Love, Alec* on the back of mine. Bonnybelle hunkers over hers for a long time before she hands it over. Wow! I finally find someone with handwriting messier than mine. It takes a while, but I finally get it. *Germs Spit & All from Bonnybelle.*

On Friday the first edition of the *Cozine Clarion* comes out. Okay, it's just a couple of mimeographed sheets, but right under the masthead it reads, *Editors: Alec Lewis & Janet Tabor*. Janet makes a fuss over the order of our names, so we agree that hers will come first on the next issue and we'll alternate after that.

I take the *Clarion* with me on my route to show to Bonnybelle, but her news tops even my debut as an editor. "Alec! Guess what?" she cries when I walk into Mrs. Phillips'. "Me an' Daddy sung fer the Rotary today, an' they paid Daddy ten whole dollars! An' Miz Barshfield, the music teacher, she was there too an' heard me. An' she said I sounded so good she wants me to do a solo fer the Christmas concert! She's a-gonna start me practicin' next week. And when we was a-leavin', the president slipped me a quarter an' said it was a special tip just fer me an' I was to spend it howsomever I wanted!"

She digs a quarter from her pocket and says, "So, Miz Phillips, Ma'am, reckon I'd like to buy two of yer best big blue jawbreakers to celebrate."

On Saturday the rain lets up enough for Bonnybelle to come with me on my route again. I pick her up shortly after ten and she rides my carrier stand down Rockwood Hill and up to Adams Street. Then she hops off and walks beside me.

She seems a lot more cheerful than last Saturday, so I ask her if she's had any more dreams about the calendar.

"Just one, an' I decided I ain't gonna let it bother me none. Yer mama's right, Alec. What's a-gonna happen is a-gonna happen, and there ain't no sense frettin' 'bout it. Me an'Mama an' Daddy are gonna sing out at the station tonight, and we're a-gonna do the best job we ever done. An' who knows? Maybe we'll get to be famous!"

She walks into Benny's like she owns the place and gazes at the rows of new and used bicycles. "Daddy says he's a-gonna put all our singin' money towards a bike fer me, so I reckon I'd better start pickin' one out. But they got so dadgum many here, Alec! How'm I ever gonna choose?"

"Well, you don't have to pick one today. They have new ones coming in every week. Just look 'em over. You've got plenty of time."

Oh Jeez! I shouldn't have said that!

For one instant that sad, fey look crosses her face. "Man, I sure do hope so!" she says

.

****

No one disputes Bonnybelle's right to go back in the *Journal* room with me, although Jill glowers at her. J. P. already has his pipe loaded and puffs clouds of Prince Albert as he sets out the stacks for us. This time eight of the gang are here early, probably just to get a look at her and tease us. Bonnybelle doesn't seem to mind. She just pulls a paper off my stack and begins folding it.

"Been a-practicin' all week with the extras Alec gives me," she tells J. P. "Been a-teachin' Cap'n Andy how to fold 'em too. He ain't very good at it, though."

"You're not afraid of him?" J. P. asks.

"Naw. He's muh friend now, thanks to Alec. He calls me Bobble, 'cause he cain't say muh name right. But I reckon he does the best he can."

"Bonnybelle," J. P. says as he puffs another cloud of Prince Albert smoke up at the ceiling. "If you were only a boy, you'd be first in line for the next route that comes up."

****

"Alec's new girlfriend is an Okie!"

Several Cozine fathers belong to the Rotary Club, so the news hits the school Monday morning. The girls all look at me again like they can't quite make up their minds to tease me about it or not.

"Yeah, but she's a singer. Daddy heard her and said she's really good!"

"My poppa said she's going to be on KMRN Wednesday night with her dad. He's supposed to be a cousin to some cowboy movie star!"

"Wow! Hey, Claudia! Would you let an Okie kiss you if his daddy was a cousin to a movie star?"

"Eeuuw no! An Okie's an Okie. It'd almost be as bad as kissing a nigger!"

At least Janet is polite enough not to question me about Bonnybelle when we work on the paper at noon, but I can tell she's plenty curious. So I show her Bonnybelle's picture, but not the writing on the back. "Hey!" Tabor says. "Is she ever cute! But there's just one thing I don't understand, Alec."

"What's that?"

"What does she see in you?"

****

It rains Monday afternoon, so I meet Bonnybelle at Mrs. Phillips'. "Hey Alec!" she greets me. "It went real good! We sung five song ballads, and Mr. Davis wants us back out there tomorrer night to do some more. Says he's a-gonna make it a double program."

"Why's he recording you tomorrow night?"

"'Cause Mama an' Daddy's goin' up to Portland Saturday to sign the papers to get Uncle Roger into the Vet's Hospital. They're gonna stay overnight an' have a fancy dinner too. Daddy got a great big check fer all the overtime he's done fer Mr. O'Dell. Ain't that neat? Me an' John Henry'll stay with the Lofgrens."

"I'd keep them here with me, but I'll be going up to Portland Thursday myself ," Mrs. Phillips says. "I've got me another new grandbaby—my youngest girl's first. So, Alec, if you'll stop the paper from Thursday to Monday, I'd appreciate it."

****

The show is called *Meet Your Neighbors,* and it airs on KMRN at 7:30 Wednesday nights. Mom, Dad and I gather around our old Philco, and I know the Wakelys and Uncle Roger will be listening with the Lofgrens. I've told J. P. and the *Journal* gang, Benny, Mrs. Carruthers and some other people on my route. My classmates already know—you can't keep a secret in a small town—and I wonder how many will tune in.

It's a good program. Ray Wakely does most of the talking and tells about learning the old traditional ballads and gospel songs from relatives in Oklahoma, Missouri and Arkansas, then listening to his own father compose new ones and finally writing them himself. Mrs. Wakely never speaks a word, just sings harmony on two of the songs. But the real star is Bonnybelle.

She begins by singing harmony on *Billy the Kid,* then sings lead on *Poor Wayfaring Stranger.* I can hear the catch in her voice as she sings the first chorus.

"I'm going there to see my brother..."

I know she's singing it for Jesse, and it prickles the hair on the back of my neck.

Sure enough, after the last chorus she says, "That song's dedicated to muh brother Jesse, who was drowned last spring down in Californey. And now we'd like to do one fer a very special boy right here in Morrisonville. Muh daddy wrote this fer me to sing, and yuh had better be a-listenin', *Mr.* Alec Lewis!"

The song, of course, is *Bandit Queen of the Badlands.* The verses, telling the story of Belle Starr's life, are just ordinary ballad lines. But when they hit the chorus, the song seems to come alive and jump out of the air at you. Bonnybelle sings lead again, and her mother harmonizes in a high, keening wail. The technique, I later learn, is called high lonesome, and it's part of a new music style being developed by an man called Bill Monroe. He calls it bluegrass.

After telling of Belle's death in a mysterious shooting (which I later research and discover goes unsolved), the Wakelys change two words in the very last line.

"That old Pale Rider has caught up to you at last."

And I shiver.

****

"I guess she's good, but what kind of music is that?"

My Cozine classmates don't know quite what to make of the program, but Mr. Hunter has no doubts. "I would pay good money to hear that family sing in concert," he tells me. "And that little girl is going to be a very big star someday!"

Janet is impressed too. "I've never heard a girl sing like that before. I'd like to meet her sometime, Alec," she says as we work on the paper during noon recess. "Too bad she doesn't go here. We could do a great story about her."

"She may wind up here. They're going to move in a few weeks."

"I hope she does," Janet says. "I could tell her a few things about you."

"Don't get any ideas about playing Lovebird with her, Janet. This girl can walk on her hands and nearly bit the thumb off a grown man when he attacked her."

"Really? She *does* sound like someone I'd like to know."

Bonnybelle shrugs off her sudden local fame. "I reckon we sounded okay, Alec," she says when I tell her how everyone raves over the program. "But wait'll yuh hear the one fer next week. It's a-gonna sound even better!"

I never do.

****

Saturday, October 15: I swing by Lofgrens to pick up Bonnybelle a little before eleven. She's waiting on the front porch with John Henry and Uncle Roger. "I cain't come with yuh today, Alec," she tells me. "Somethin' awful's done happened."

"What is it?"

"Mr. Lofgren got took real sick this mornin'. Miz Lofgren hadta take him to the hospital, so I gotta stay here and mind John Henry till she comes back."

"All right, I'll see you when I come by."

J. P. and the crew are disappointed she's not with me. "That little girl can flat-out sing," J. P. says as he fires up his old pipe. "Takes me back to when I was a boy in Indiana." Frank and Don at the barber shop have compliments for her too, and Mrs. Carruthers is about as enthusiastic as a librarian is allowed to get.

"Pure folk art!" she tells me. "The whole family should be on *Ted Mack's Amateur Hour*! And if that little girl isn't good enough for *Stars of Tomorrow*, then I don't know what the world is coming to!"

There is still no sign of Mrs. Lofgren when I reach Rockwood Hill. "Where are you going to stay tonight?" I ask Bonnybelle.

"In the trailer, I guess. Miz Lofgren's done locked her house, and Miz Phillips is up in Portland. So we ain't got no choice."

"Let me go down to the hospital and see when she'll be back. Hey! Maybe you could stay at our place, Bonnybelle.I could ask Mom and—"

"Nope. Don't reckon Uncle Roger'd let me, an' I gotta mind him when Mama an' Daddy ain't here. 'Sides, John Henry allus squalls when I leave him alone with Uncle Roger."

"I'll check and come back. Maybe we can figure something out."

I race back to the hospital and hunt for Mrs. Lofgren. When I finally find her, she shakes her head. "They're getting set to operate on him, Alec," she says. "It doesn't look good. I'm probably gonna be stuck here all night. They'll be safe enough in the trailer with their uncle. You know he'd never do anything to hurt either of them."

That may be true, but I still feel a sense of dread gnawing at me. I ride home to ask Mom if they can stay with us. Dad is home for lunch, and they both say no.

"We can't do that unless their uncle asks us to," Dad says. "In the absence of their parents, he's the closest adult relative and their guardian in the eyes of the law. If we brought them here without his consent, we'd be kidnapping them. Don't worry, Son. It's just for one night."

So I have to go back and tell Bonnybelle that we can't take them in either. "Do you know where they're staying up in Portland?" I ask her. "Maybe we could call."

"Naw. That's okay, Alec. Yuh done yer best. Reckon me an' John Henry'll be safe enough fer one night. I kin allus lock the door."

"But he can lock you in from the other side."

"That's all right. I scrounged up an' ol' coffee can fer us to use if'n we cain't get out to the toilet. Wouldn't be the first time. I just wish…"

"What?"

"Wish I had me a jawbreaker to swap with yuh fer luck."

"I'll go down to Stannard's and get us a couple."

"Naw. The magic won't work less'n they're Miz Phillips' big blue ones." She forces a smile. "We kin get 'em when she comes back Monday. Fer now, I reckon we'll hafta say goodbye the ol'-fashioned way, if'n it won't make yuh turn all red."

"It won't," I say quietly, and kiss her goodbye. Then I get back on my bike and pedal off into the October drizzle.

****

Sunday, October 16: The rain is holding off, for the moment at least, but I can feel it in the air as I bump my bike down the front steps and make for O'Dell's Flying-A. I've never quite been able to shake the spooky feeling that rides with me in the darkness for the first few blocks. I think it's the silence, the utter absence of movement and life in a small town before dawn on a Sunday morning, that weighs down on me. Usually it goes away as soon as I reach Third Street and see the lights up at the hotel and the garage, but this morning it stays with me.

J. P. puffs quietly at his pipe and checks us off as we show up one by one. Ferraday, Dixon and Reed are quietly loading papers. They nod at me, but nobody says anything. I wish Dirty Dave would show up. I could use a joke, even one of his old ones, to break up this feeling of dread growing inside me. But why do I feel it? What can happen in a small town before dawn on a Sunday morning? But there's no sign of Archer yet, so I load up and head out.

I can probably do Route 3 in my sleep by now, daily or Sunday. On the big covered porch at the Elks Club, I tuck the upper right corner of the *Journal* under *The Oregonian* that's already there—partly to keep the wind from blowing it open and partly to give them the impression that I get there first. At the police station the night dispatcher is on the phone. He doodles and scribbles on a pad as he mutters an occasional "Umm-hmm" and "Yes, Ma'am." I get a quick wave, but that's all.

I get the library and the houses on Second Street and then pause. Like Madigan, I like to wait for sunup before doing Rockwood Hill. But today some force seems to be pushing me on, so I ride down across the Star Mill and turn onto the old white bridge in the just-before-dawn blackness. I hear a splash and the cry of an animal down along Cozine Creek beneath the bridge, but I can't tell what it is.

This is stupid, I tell myself. *Nothing is happening, and nothing is going to to happen.* I can see lights in one house—not one of my subscribers—but all the others are dark, just as I expect and just as they should be. I can barely make out the outline of the old trailer in Mr. Lofgren's back yard. It looks the same as it has every Sunday morning I've come up here.

And yet why is the hair prickling on the back of my neck?

The sky begins to lighten in the east. By the time I finish the deliveries, it will be light enough to see clearly. Then I can swing back for one last look before heading home. I roll the last Rockwood Hill paper into a cylinder and shove it in a *Journal* tube under a mailbox. Then I ride back to Lofgren's. Everything is still just as it should be.

Then I see it.

Smoke! Just a thin line—a wisp, perhaps, or a tendril—seeping through a crack in the roof, but it has no business being there. I try to convince myself that it's an illusion or a mirage, but it isn't. There's a fire in that trailer, and Bonnybelle, her brother and her uncle are asleep in there!

It's almost like the time I make the catch at Vaughn Street Stadium. I'm off the bike, racing for the trailer and pounding on the door before I realize what I'm doing. "Fire!" I yell. "Fire! Bonnybelle! Roger! Wake up! Get out!"

There's no response. I remember Bonnybelle telling me that if her uncle takes a heavy dose of medication, it's just about impossible to wake him up until it wears off. I try the door, but it's locked. So I race around to the back. There are two steps up into the trailer, so from outside Bonnybelle's window is more than a foot above my head. I hammer on the window with my fists, but someone has replaced the glass with plastic, and it won't break.

Bonnybelle's face appears above me and I hear her yell, "What is it?"

"Fire! Get out quick!" I yell back. Her face disappears, then reappears a moment later.

"Cain't! Uncle Rdoger's locked us in! We're trapped!"

"The window! Can you get it open?"

"I'll try. Can yuh help?"

"It's too high! I can barely reach it!" I look around desperately for something to stand on, something to give me an extra foot or two. There it is—a wheelbarrow!

A light comes on in the house next door. An elderly woman pokes her head out and demands, "What's all the commotion here?"

I point to the smoke, which is already thicker. "The trailer's on fire!" I yell at her. "There are people inside!"

She puts a hand to her mouth, and I hear her gasp, "Ohmygoodnessohmygoodness!"

"Call the fire department. Quick!"

"Yesyesyesyesofccurse!" she gasps and vanishes, while I grab the wheelbarrow, roll it over beneath the window and jump in it.

That gives me another two feet to work with. Bonnybelle is doing her best to pry the window open. It's supposed to slide sideways on a metal track, but the frame must be warped. She only has it open a couple of inches, but that's enough for me to work my fingers inside and add my strength to hers. Slowly, an inch or two at a time, the opening widens, but the draft it creates begins to draw the smoke under her door.

John Henry wakes up and begins to squall, while I try to coordinate our efforts. "One-two-three—*heave!*" I cry. "One-two-three—*heave!*" We make progress, but it's maddingly slow.

All the while I'm thinking, *Why doesn't the siren go off? Why won't someone come to help? Is everyone asleep?*

A last "One-two-three—*heave!*" and the window is open as wide as it's going to go. I measure it quickly with my eyes. Maybe, just *maybe*, it's enough. "Come on, Bonnybelle!" I plead. "Time to get you outa there!"

"Wait!" she cries. "John Henry goes first!" She's coughing now as the smoke gets thicker, but she grabs her little brother and boosts him up to the window. John Henry cries and kicks, but she manages to shove his head and shoulders past the frame. I grab hold of him and pull, none too gently, and he slides out into my arms, wearing nothing but a tiny t-shirt and a diaper.

"Don't move!" I order as I set him on the ground and turn back to helpBonnybelle.

I can hear coughing and yelling beind her now. Uncle Roger must be awake and blundering around the main room. I hope he can find the front door. The window is big enough for John Henry, *maybe* big enough for Bonnybelle, but clearly impossible for him.

Why doesn't the dad-blamed siren go off?

Bonnybelle sticks her head through the opening and says, "Yer gonna hafta help me, Alec. It's a-gonna be a mighty tight squeeze!"

"Give me your hands, then." I pull, she squirms, but we don't make much progress. Her head and neck are clear, and her arms are out up past her elbows, but her shoulders are a problem. Bonnybelle is not a small, frail thing like Mary Alice. A girl who can walk on her hands and has been working in the fields for years has well-developed arms and shoulders, even at eleven.

"One-two-three—*heave!*" I chant. "One-two-three—*heave!*" Then, thank God, I hear the siren go off.

"Hang on, Bonnybelle! The cavalry's on the way!"

"Yer scrapin' muh hide off, but I reckon we're a-gonna make it. C'mon! One-two-three—*heave!*" The siren continues to wail as we slowly work her free. I hear a crash in the other room as Uncle Roger stumbles into something. *Find the front door, Roger!* I'm thinking as I pull on Bonnybelle. *It must be hell in there, but I can't help you!*

At least her head is outside so she can breathe. The smoke must be awfully thick behind her. Then her shoulders are clear, and it looks like we're going to make it. Bonnybelle even manages a grin as she continues to squirm.

"Just lost a little hide is all. Good thing muh boobs ain't a-growin much yet, huh? Reckon that'd be *mighty* uncomfortable. Aw shoot!"

"What is it?"

"Just realized I don't have nothin on but this here t-shirt and them ol' drawers with the big rip in the back. Looks like yer a-gonna be seein' muh bee-hind sooner'n I'd planned on!"

"I promise I won't look!" I tell her as I continue to pull.

"Just get me outa here, Alec, and yuh kin look all yuh want!"

I brace myself for a final tug that will pull her all the way free. Then there's another crash and smoke pours out through every inch of the opening that Bonnybelle isn't filling. Uncle Roger has found the door, but it's the wrong one. Bonnybelle screams as she starts sliding back into the trailer, and I realize that Roger has her by the legs and is pulling against me. I try to fight him, but he is stronger and has better leverage. Her shoulders scrape back through and she vanishes into the smoke, but I still manage to keep hold of one wrist.

"No, Roger!" I yell as I struggle to keep a grip. "You can't get her out the other way. Put her through the window! She'll fit!"

Uncle Roger's face suddenly appears through the smoke. His eyes are wide open, but they don't see me. Maybe he'sback in the hell of Kasserine Pass or some German *stalag*. Maybe he thinks I'm one of the men who attack Bonnybelle down in California. He grabs my right arm and twists it until I let go of her wrist. Then he pulls and slams my head against the side of the trailer.

Pure cold fear shoots through me. This is no longer a case of saving someone else. My own life is on the line now. Roger has me pinned against the side of the trailer, and he's trying to pull me around to where he can get at my throat with his other hand. The only thing saving me is the smoke, which is now pouring out so thickly that he can't see. How does he even breathe? How much longer can I?

Then I'm aware of someone in the wheelbarrow beside me, and that someone is pulling me back the other way. My right arm feel like it's being torn loose. A freak breeze blows the smoke clear for an instant, and I see Roger's face again and those blank, dead eyes looking past me into another world. Then there's a blur and something slams into his face, once, twice, three times. *Splap! Splap! Splap!* It sounds like Mr. King, the butcher, tenderizing meat with his mallet.

Uncle Roger's eyes snap into focus, and he releases my arm. Then the wind shifts again and I get a lungful of smoke. Next thing I know, I'm lying on the ground. Someone is holding me and crying, "Arric! Arric! Where Bobble?"

Then the cavalry finally arrives, and they have the fire out in less than five minutes.

More sirens. The police, then an ambulance, then people as the gawkers come out to stare. Cap'n Andy keeps hold of me and pleads, "Arric hurt! Help Arric!" John Henry is screaming too, but the firemen concentrate on getting Bonnybelle and her uncle out of the now-smoldering trailer. Cap'n Andy's punches bring Roger back to reality, and I guess he realizes what he has done. His last act is to cover Bonnybelle with his own body to shield her from the fire, and he succeeds in protecting her from the flames. She's burned a little on one foot, but otherwise unmarked.

But he can't shield her from the smoke and all the poisons and gasses in it. By the time the firemen get them out, Roger is obviously dead, and Bonnybelle isn't breathing.

Trained paramedics with 21st-century technology could probably revive her, but in 1953 ambulance drivers aren't paramedics and that technology does not exist. They load her in the ambulance and make a quick run to the hospital, but the doctors there pronounce Bonnybelle dead on arrival.

Chapter Sixteen: Year's End

I don't learn of Bonnybelle's death for several hours. Officer D arrives right behind the ambulance, takes one look at me, bundles me into his car and tears off to the hospital. My right shoulder feels like it's been torn loose, and that's pretty close to what has happened. A doctor sticks something over my face, and the next thing I know it's early afternoon. I'm lying in a strange bed with my arm strapped to my side in some kind of harness.

I can sense there are people around me, but my eyes don't want to open. So I struggle to sit up. *Big* mistake! I get hit with the worst case of the dry-heaves I ever experience.

"That's the anesthetic," I hear a strange voice say. "Ether does that every time."

"Will he be all right?" Hey! That sounds like Mom.

"Give him a minute. He'll be fine."

The wave of nausea passes and my eyes finally decide to work. Mom and Dad are beside my bed, along with Grandma and Grandpa Fullerton. And Aunt Emma Snyder is here too. And J. P. and Officer D. What is going on?

A woman in a white starched uniform gently wipes my face with a damp cloth. "There," she says. "Feel better now?"

"What happened? Where am I?"I know it sounds corny, but I actually say that.

"You're in the hospital with a dislocated shoulder and a possible concussion," the nurse says. "How you came to get them? Well, that's what everyone wants to know. The only ones who can answer that are you, Bertram Slade and a two-year-old boy, and we can't get a word of sense out of either of them."

"What about Bonnybelle and her uncle?"

"I'm sorry, Honey. They didn't make it."

It takes a minute for that to sink in and register. Bonnybelle has gone out of my life—forever. *"That old pale rider has caught up to you..."* But, Dear God! Why does it have to be so soon? I hate to cry in front of people, but I can't help it.

"It was so close!" I manage to say between sobs. "I almost had her! One more good pull..."

"Just start at the beginning and tell us what happened," Officer D urges.

"Yessir." I tell them everything I can remember, from my uneasy feeling that morning, to seeing that first wisp of smoke, to Cap'n Andy pulling me free from Uncle Roger's grip. Officer D interrupts me once.

"Are you positive the smoke was coming from *inside* the trailer and the door was locked?"

"Yessir. I'm sure of it."

"Then that lets Bertram Slade off the hook. We're holding him on suspicion of arson and murder, but if you're sure the fire was coming from the inside..."

"Double-dang, certain-for-sure positive, Sir." It's one of Bonnybelle's favorite phrases that I pick up on and will use the rest of my life. "Cap'n Andy—Mr. Slade—would never hurt Bonnybelle. She was always nice to him."

"Hmm. I wonder why he was out there so early? Well, that's one we'll never know, I guess. Anyway, Alec, the little boy is fine. You saved his life."

"Nosir. Bonnybelle did. She would have made it out, but she stayed behind to help him."

"Greater love hath no man than this..." Aunt Emma says softly.

"Make sure you tell the reporters that," J. P. adds.

"Reporters?"

"Yes. The *Journal* has a man here. So does *The Oregonian* and the *Morrisonville Register.* The Salem papers will probably be over too. They're outside waiting for you to get strong enough to talk to 'em."

"They act like it's the end of the world they're covering," the nurse sniffs. "You don't have to see them if you don't feel up to it."

"I will, in a minute. But how long do I have to wear this?" I indicate the harness.

"The doctor will tell you for sure, but I'd say a couple of weeks." She finally manages a tiny smile. "You'll just be starting to get good with your left hand when you go back to the right." Then she turns Mom and Dad and goes all serious again. "We want to keep him here for awhile. He got a lungful of that smoke, and there's no telling what sort of stuff was in it. And those bruises where he was smacked against the side of the trailer look pretty nasty."

"Pietrowski says he'll do your route until you can come back," J. P. adds. "Freeman already knows his, so we'll be able to cover for you."

Now I'm feeling useless on top of everything else. "I'll be back tomorrow," I tell him, "and I'd like to go home now."

"This evening, *if* Doctor says it's okay," the nurse repeats.

Aunt Emma kisses me on the forehead. "I've got to get back to Portland for the evening service, but I'll be back tomorrow," she promises me. "He's going to need a lot of help getting through this week," she says to Mom and Dad. "Believe me. I won't intrude on your own minister, but I've helped people through the loss of a loved one more times than I care to remember."

"A loved one?" Dad starts to protest, but she cuts him off.

"Henry, puppy love is very real if you're a puppy. Losing a first crush to death at eleven probably hurts as much as losing a husband at thirty-three. That was my age when Samuel was killed over in Spain. The only good thing is that the young recover quickly." She runs a hand gently over my face. "Just like your other injuries, Alec. They will heal, but the memories will remain. You have good memories of her, don't you?"

"I do, Aunt Emma."

"Hang onto them then."

Aunt Emma's leaving triggers a general exodus. Mom and Dad stay behind to help me with the reporters. "Be nice to all of them," J. P. says as he leaves, "but I'll tell the *Journal* man to stay behind if you have anything extra just for him."

"I've got a picture of her in my wallet, but I don't know where my pants are—and I want it back!"

"I'll see to it," Mom says.

The reporters are kind and their questions polite, but I can tell they've done this many times before, and they're no strangers to other people's misery. "Please!" I say to them. "Make sure you say how she stayed behind to get her little brother out. I—I guess she gave up her life for him."

I look over at Mom and suddenly remember her words from last spring. *"It's called a sacrifice, like the batter who gives himself up to advance the runner."*

Oh Lord! Could I ever love someone that much?

****

I manage to talk the doctor into letting me go home that night, but I have to sleep propped up on extra pillows so I won't roll on the injured shoulder. I learn next morning that some very private functions are either going to require some help or else a lot of extra time. Dad stays behind to help me get dressed and ties my shoes for me. I insist on riding my bike to school, so he takes it down from the porch and follows me in the car to make sure I get there safely.

Class has already started when I walk into Mr. Hunter's room, but everything stops and Mr. Hunter walks over and shakes my left hand with his. "The left side is closer to the heart anyway, Alec," he says. "We didn't expect you back today."

I try a smile, but it doesn't really come off. "No fun just sitting around home feeling sorry for myself," I mutter.

"I just read the class the article in *The Oregonian*. How's your arm?"

"Dislocated shoulder. I won't be able to use it for a couple of weeks."

"Think you can write left-handed?"

"You know how bad I am with the right, but I'll try."

"No need. I'll excuse you from homework, and I'll give you oral tests. Alec, I'm so sorry about Bonnybelle. I know she was, well, a special friend."

"She was my girlfriend, Mr. Hunter. I really liked—no. I loved her." There! I say it right in front of the class, and I feel a little better for doing it.

"Mr. Hunter," I continue. "Can I ask the class something?"

"Certainly."

"I'm going to need help doing my paper route tonight. Would any boy in here be willing to come along and help out?"

"Any boy on the football team who would like to help Alec will be excused from practice," Mr. Hunter adds. Every boy in the class puts his hand up. I choose Larry Dale and promise to pick a different person every day until they've all had a chance. Man! Just like Tom Sawyer getting his aunt's fence whitewashed!

Even with the support of my classmates, it's an awfully tough morning. I have to concentrate all the time, because whenever my attention wanders I see Bonnybelle trying to work her way through the window and joking as she struggles for her life.

Lunch? Well, it could be worse. We have chili and cornbread, which Cliff Kilgore butters for me after he opens my milk carton. I'm slowly getting used to the fact that I'm going to have to depend on others for help. It's either that or stay home and see Bonnybelle in that window whenever I close my eyes.

After lunch Mr. Hunter tells me to stay in the room and work on the paper with Janet. "If you just want to talk, I'll see that you're not disturbed," he tells us. I can sense he wants me to open up to someone, but why does he pick Janet?

Tabor and I sit across the table from each other, make a quick eye contact and then look away, like we've each caught the other in an embarrassing position and don't want to say the wrong thing. Yet we have to say something.

"Alec, you must really hurt," she finally says.

"Yeah, I do."

"Is there anything I can do to help?"

"Could you maybe just listen while I talk about her and not tell anyone what I said?"

"Sure. Go ahead."

So I let it all pour out—from the time I meet her at Lofgren's, introducing her to Mrs. Phillips, how proud she is when she gets new school clothes, even though they're used and how she runs beside me on my route and makes friends with Cap'n Andy. I tell her about the dinner, the first time Bonnybelle ever gets to dress up, how she accidently drenches herself in Mrs. Phillips' perfume and how we wind up listening to *The Whistler* in the dark. I even tell her about how we swap jawbreakers.

Janet doesn't say anything. We've been rivals—sometimes friendly, usually not—since the first grade. She's usually the top student in the class and I'm second. But every once in a while I beat her, and Janet does not like to lose.

Now when I look at her I see a new expression, like she actually cares about me. Her face looks, well, almost tender.

I've never seen that look on Janet before, and it startles me for a moment.

"Go on," she says.

So I tell her about Bonnybelle's dream of her brother Jesse and the dream about the calendars going blank and how they both come true. By this time I'm close to crying, and Janet's eyes are wet too.

"We came so close! Just a few more seconds! One more good tug!" I stand up and turn away so she won't see me crying, but she comes around behind me and puts her arms around me just below the harness.

"But you did save her little brother, Alec. That makes you a hero in my book."

She squeezes me a little tighter and I giggle. I can't help it.

"I'm not tickling you, am I?"

"No, you just reminded me of something. I guess it's not really funny, but—"

"What is it?"

"I don't think you'd really like to know."

"How will I know that unless you tell me. Go ahead."

"Well, I was trying to pull her out, and we'd just worked her shoulders free, and she said it was a good thing her boobs hadn't grown much or it'd get awful painful when we scraped 'em through the window frame. And then when you hugged me just now, your own b—"

Oh jeez! I just said *boobs* to a girl! Boys aren't supposed to do that in 1953.

Janet places her right hand against my face and slides it along my cheek. "There!" she says. "I'll give you a real slap when you have two hands to defend yourself." Then she giggles too. "I hope you're convinced now that it's me and not kleenex. Oh man! Going through a window like that *would* hurt!"

That sets off another round of giggles. "And right after that she got mad because all she had on was a t-shirt and drawers with a big rip in the back. I told her I wouldn't look."

"But I bet you would have!" We're both a little embarrassed at where the conversation is going. When you're not quite twelve in 1953, you're pretty self-conscious about your body. But at least I'm smiling a bit, so Janet plows ahead.

"Alec, I don't think you'll ever see me hanging upside down from a window in my undies. But if it ever happened, I hope I'd be worth looking at."

"I'd pay lots of money to see it," I tell her.

"You couldn't come up with enough!" she says,and we giggle again. Then the mood shifts and we're serious once more.

"Alec, do you know why I've always hated you up to now?"

"Why?"

"Because you're the only one in the whole grade who can beat me at things."

"Not very often," I remind her.

"But you can sometimes. I've always felt you could do it any time if you thought I was worth the trouble. It's like you were shrugging me off and saying, 'Oh, I'm just letting you win'."

"No. I think it's because I've always been a little scared of you."

"Don't be." Again she places her hand on my cheek. "Alec, I think you need a big sister. Can I be that for you?"

"Janet, I'm a couple of months older than you are."

She draws herself up to her full height. "Yeah, but I *am* bigger, at least for now. I'd like to help you with your route tonight too."

"Larry Dale is already coming."

"Then let me come too. Please, Alec! I'll even shake hands with the creep."

"Okay, Sis. Call your mom and then come down to Benny's with us."

****

I call Mom right after school to reassure her that I'm okay and that I have two helpers who will do the route with me. She tells me that Aunt Emma Snyder is back and is making funeral arrangements for Bonnybelle. The Veterans of Foreign Wars will bury Uncle Roger in their cemetery up by Beaverton. He kills Bonnybelle and nearly kills me, but he also fights for his country.

"Aunt Emma will explain when you get home," Mom says. "She's in charge of things."

"What about Bonnybelle's mom and dad?"

"I'm afraid they can't be part of it," Mom says, and I'm left wondering why.

Larry, Janet and I ride down to Benny's together. All talking stops when we walk in, and the hush follows us clear back to the *Journal* room, where I introduce my helpers to J. P. and the crew. Ferraday hands me a paper and silently points to the story—below the fold, but on the front page. Our school pictures stare back at me. The caption under Bonnybelle's reads, "Gives life for brother." The one under mine says, "Heroic carrier saves one." I don't feel one bit like a hero. I should have saved her too, but I fail, and I don't want to read about it.

Archer starts to tell a joke, then thinks better of it and begins showing Larry how to fold the papers. I feel useless again and look around for something to do or someone to talk to. The other carriers look away, unable to meet my eyes, but I can read their thoughts. *Here is someone who has looked death in the face, who has seen a friend die. He's different now. It has marked him, and he's no longer like the rest of us.*

J. P. finally puts a hand on my good shoulder and says, "If there's anything the boys and I can do to help out, you just let us know. Are you sure you'll be all right?"

It's Janet who answers. "Don't worry, Mr. Harrington. We won't let anything happen to him." As Larry carries the bags out for me, Jill runs up and grabs my left arm. Tears spill out of her eyes and run down her cheeks.

"Alec!" she cries. "I did a terrible thing! When I saw her go back there Saturday, I got so mad that I wished she would die—and then she did!"

"It's all right, Jill. I know you didn't really mean it."

"Please Alec! Call me Twerp!"

****

I guess you never find out how caring people can be until you really need it. As we stop at the shops along the route, everyone pauses for a kind word or a pat on the shoulder (the good one, fortunately). Mom Jenkins gives us each a popcorn ball, and the clerk at Stannard's slices three slivers off the big wheel of cheese they keep by the counter. Officer D offers to drive me Sunday morning. Mrs. Carruthers is too choked up to say anything.

When we reach Rockwood Hill, I change the pattern so I won't have to ride past Lofgren's and the burnt-out trailer. Mrs. Lofgren is still down at the hospital with her husband—who recovers and lives another ten years—so I give Larry the number and he gets it for me.

Then Cap'n Andy pedals up on his old black bike, and I mutter, "Jeez! We forgot his extra." He spends a few hours in jail, but the police release him once Officer D relays the information that I see the smoke coming from inside the trailer. To me Cap'n Andy is the hero. If he isn't there to pull me loose, I'd probably be dead now too.

"Arric!" he cries. "You okay?"

"Yes, thanks to you, Mr. Slade." I introduce him to Larry and Janet. "Be real nice to him," I urge. "He probably saved my life yesterday."

"Would you like to come with us and help finish up?" Janet asks as she shakes his hand.

Cap'n Andy nods eagerly. Then his mood changes and he wails, "Poor Bobble. Not fair!"

He's right, of course. The fire marshal determines that Uncle Roger causes the blaze by falling asleep on the couch while smoking. The lit cigarette lands on an old rug and probably smolders for an hour or two before taking hold, and Uncle Roger is so heavily medicated that he doesn't wake up until it's too late for him—and Bonnybelle.

No one can locate the Wakelys in Portland to tell them, so the police are waiting when they return Sunday afternoon, right about the time I'm waking up in the hospital. Mrs. Wakely collapses and never comes out of it. She does what I once tell Janet I want to do. She crawls into a hole and pulls it in after her. She winds up at the mental hospital in Salem and never leaves it.

Ray Wakely goes back to the bottle. I don't know how he gets one in Morrisonville on a Sunday, but he does. He gets roaring drunk, takes off in his old car and piles it up against a tree. Maybe he intends to kill himself, but he doesn't quite succeed. They bring him into the hospital about the time I'm getting out. He's in for several weeks and refuses all visitors except one. When he's finally released, he drifts away like a withered leaf in the November wind. No one ever hears from him again. The State of Oregon takes temporary custody of John Henry.

Mom and Aunt Emma explain the situation when I get home from the route. "We are about the closest thing to family that she has now," Mom says, and I think, *Has? Now?* There is no more present or future for Bonnybelle. It's over. Done. Finished.

Aunt Emma must guess what I'm thinking. "Alec," she says. "The service is for the benefit of the living, not the dead. She is with God now. Can you believe that and keep it with you?"

"I want to, Aunt Emma! But I don't think she ever went to church…"

"Maybe so. But I heard her sing those gospel songs. Your father got me copies of the tapes. Jesus appreciates good music."

My eyes are tearing up again. "They were going to let her sing a solo at the Christmas Concert. She was learning *O Holy Night*, and..." I can't finish the sentence. I break down and bawl like a baby.

"And she will sing it, Alec!" she says as she gently puts an arm around me. "And think of the audience she will have!"

****

Aunt Emma schedules the service for Friday morning at our church. I've never seen her sober, serious and at work before, and it's a real eye-opener for me. She drives back and forth to Portland at least once a day (and this before freeways). When she's here, she's constantly on the phone—organizing, begging, badgering and bullying.

"Don't worry," she tells Mom. "My congregation and radio listeners will pay your phone bill this month. I'm splicing two of her songs into this week's broadcast and making a special appeal at the Wednesday service. All expenses will be covered."

Criminy! I think as I watch her plow through obstacles. With her on the Loyalist side, how do Franco and the Falangists ever manage to win in Spain?

I don't contribute very much at home, at school or on the route. It's almost like I'm sleepwalking through the week. The pills the doctor gives me for pain probably have something to do with it. Dad helps me get dressed. Breakfast is either cereal or hotcakes—something I can eat lefthanded without making too big a mess. School is listening, answering, concentrating so I won't think back and talking with Janet at noon.

By Wednesday she really is becoming a big sister to me, but nothing more than that. After I open up to her, she finally confides in me.

"There's this boy I really like," she says. "He goes to my church, but my folks won't let me see him because he's in the eighth grade."

"Does he like you?"

"I think so. He always talks to me after the service, and he smiles at me a lot."

"That doesn't mean much. I'm talking with you right now."

"But don't you understand, Alec? He's *taller* than I am!"

A different boy helps with the route every day, but Janet always comes too. By Thursday she could probably manage the route herself, but J. P. is adamant. My official helper has to be a boy. He makes a big point of buying each one a pepsi when I introduce them. Then, as a casual afterthought, he slips Janet a dime and says, "Here. You might as well get yourself one too." Janet takes me aside and tells me the only reason she does is that her folks won't let her have soda pop at home.

****

Mom and Aunt Emma don't want me to see Bonnybelle until just before the service. "There's nothing there but an empty vessel," Aunt Emma says. "The true Bonnybelle is a spirit with God now. You can't see her, but she can see you. And she can hear you every time you pray." I don't know if I believe that. But, Oh Lord! I sure *want* to believe it!

I'm dreading having to see her for the last time. How do I say goodbye to someone who isn't there? On Thursday I figure out what to do.

I don't think more than a handful of people will come to the service. Her folks can't. Her uncle is dead, and we don't know where John Henry is. Mrs. Lofgren probably will, though Mr. Lofgren is still in the hospital. Mrs. Phillips will, of course. Maybe her teacher and a few of her classmates will be there. Well, I underestimate the power of the press, the radio and my Aunt Emma Snyder.

KMRN runs a special program featuring her songs and interviews with people, including me, who knew her. KPOJ picks it up and rebroadcasts it from Portland. The

Morrisonville Register runs a couple of feature articles and a long editorial about her. They call her, "The Little Wayfaring Stranger who graced our community for seven weeks." I don't hear Aunt Emma's program, since her station doesn't have a signal strong enough to reach Morrisonville, but it must be powerful stuff.

The First Presbyterian Church is packed by one o'clock Friday afternoon. Aunt Emma browbeats our minister into holding the service there and letting her conduct it. Mrs. Lofgren and Mrs. Phillips are there along with Mom and Dad and me—and Janet, who begs to be allowed to sit with us. "It's so strange," she says as we walk in. "I never met her and yet, after talking with you this week, I feel like I've known her all my life."

Cap'n Andy is there too, with his councilman uncle, and he's actually bathed and shaved and wearing clean clothes. Then I see Benny and Mrs, Benson and Jill, and J. P. and several of the *Journal* carriers who have gotten out of school. Mom Jenkins and Mrs. Carruthers have come. Mr. O'Dell is there, and Officer D and Frank from the barber shop. At least thirty of her classmates from Fox Glen are there. Then people like Janet, dozens of them, who may not have met her at all—yet they feel like they've known her all her life.

I am to be the last one to see her before they close the coffin for the service. They have her in a little room off the main sanctuary, and I ask Janet to come with me. "I've never seen someone dead before," I admit as we walk down the hall. "Have you?"

"Once, when I was five. My great-grandmother. She was awful old and in a nursing home. I think I only saw her once when she was alive."

"What did she look like?"

"Like a big wax doll. You've heard people say they look like they're asleep? Huh-uh! I've watched my dad when he slept on the couch. I could see his chest move when he breathed, and he'd make little sounds sometimes, and his nose would twitch. When they're dead, they're totally still and totally quiet. Kinda spooky!"

"What do they feel like?"

"I don't know. I never—Alec! Are you going to…to…?"

"I have to. There's something I have to give her. Will you promise not to tell?"

"Are you kidding? I won't even watch!"

They've closed the door to the viewing room, but the man beside it recognizes me and lets us in. It's the first time I see Bonnybelle since last Sunday morning, and it's that last time that I or anyone else on this earth will ever see her.

She's wearing the same white dress she wears to the dinner, but Aunt Emma and Janet are right. It's just an empty vessel, a big wax doll that the real Bonnybell has left behind. She's somewhere trying out her new form and her new voice. I wonder if she gets wings, like the pictures of angels I color back in Sunday School when I'm little. I know she'd get a kick out of them. I hope God gives her some good ones.

Then it's time to say goodbye. I take one of Mrs. Phillips' big blue jawbreakers from my pocket and put it in my mouth. Janet retreats to the door and turns her back. When the jawbreaker is good and sticky, I take it out and carefully place it in Bonnybelle's hand, which is cold and feels a little bit like modeling clay.

"Love you forever, Bonnybelle," I whisper. "Germs and spit and all." Then I rejoin Janet and we walk back into the sanctuary together.

****

People cope with loss in different ways at different times. If I'm older and living in the 60's or 70's, I might easily take to drugs and ruin my own life. But being a child of the 50's, I cover the pain by becoming Joe Superstudent. Janet may be a friend and a big sister now, but she's never going to top me again in anything, if I can help it.

I also force myself to keep the journal going for Aunt Emma. Mom puts in the articles about Bonnybelle and the fire and then staples those pages together. "Someday you'll be ready to read them," she tells me. "You can pull the staples then. But this has become a valuable document. It's a history of what may be the most important year in your life. Please keep it up!"

So I add articles about the cold war in Europe, Senator McCarthy's feud with Former President Truman and the downfall and execution of Lavrenti Beria, a particularly nasty Russian and the former head of Stalin's secret police. But no more quirkies make it in. I'm not much interested in laughter during the last two months of 1953.

I can't listen to *The Whistler* anymore either. I try it once, but when I hear those thirteen notes, it's like I can feel Bonnybelle snuggling against me and I can hear her saying,"I kin stand it, but I'd be mighty obliged if'n yuh'd put an arm 'round me."

I guess I've heard the last of *The Whistler*.

Someone gets a copy of the article to Mary Alice, and she writes me a long letter saying how proud she is to know me and what a great guy I am. But there's a subtle difference in her tone now. She talks about the new friends she has and how wonderful the new school is, and there is no mention of wanting to come back to Morrisonville. We have come to the point where the two roads diverge in the wood. She's taking one and I'm taking the other, and the two roads will probably never intersect again.

I need something, but I'm not sure what it is. Absolution would be close, but we're not Catholics, so that's out. Counseling? Child psychologists don't inhabit small Oregon towns in 1953. Our minister talks with me. He's an old man, good and decent at heart, but not up to dealing with the forces raging inside a not-quite-twelve-year-old who is sure he's a failure.

I remember what Mrs. Chivington says to Janet and Peggy and me after the incident with Davey Scroggins. *"You almost did a noble deed. You came oh, so close, but you failed."*

And I remember being up at Vaughn Street in 1952. Bottom of the ninth, two out, one on, the Beavers down by one and Joe Brovia coming up against the Padres. You'd think they'd walk him, but no. They pitch to him, and he almost makes them pay. Joe belts a towering drive to the deepest part of center field, and I remember the roar that goes up when it leaves his bat. But the center fielder catches it even as he slams into the fence, and the roar turns to a groan as the game ends and the Beavers lose. Poor Joe. Poor me. We come oh, so close—but we fail.

My mood brightens a little the first week in November when the harness comes off and I can use my right arm again. Then, on Saturday the 6th, absolution finally arrives.

Another old rattletrap of a car, with Missouri plates this time, pulls up in front of our house. It's mid-afternoon and I've just finished my route. A man gets out and knocks at our door. When Dad answers, the man introduces himself as Robert Wakely.

"I'm Ray Wakely's brother," he tells us. "Come out to pick up John Henry, 'cause Ray an' his wife won't be able to care for him no more. I understand a young man who saved John Henry's life lives here, an' I'd like to thank him."

"Yes indeed," Dad says. "Won't you come in?"

United Press International picks up the *Journal*'s story and sends it around the country, eventually to reach Ray Wakely's brother back in Missouri. There's no doubt of the relationship. I look into Robert Wakely's face and I can see Ray and John Henry—and a little bit of Bonnybelle too.

"Me an' muh wife got a little farm 'bout twenty miles outa Joplin," he tells us. "She's back there takin' care of our three kids while I come out here to get John Henry. Ray an' his wife's too busted up to care for him no more. We ain't got much, but he'll be with his kinfork, an' he'll be loved."

"Will the State of Oregon release him to you?" Dad asks.

"I got in to talk to Ray yesterday. He done signed the papers, an' I'll be a-leavin' with John Henry tonight. But afore I go, I wanta shake this here young man's hand—Alec's yer name, ain't it? An' I wanta thank yuh fer savin' John Henry. Don't hold it against Ray that he ain't thanked yuh hisself. He loved all his kids, but Bonnybelle was his favorite, an' losin' her's just tore him all apart."

"I loved her too, Mr. Wakely."

"Bet yuh did, Son. From what I hear, she was a right cute li'l thing. Wish there was a pitcher or somethin' I could take back with me."

"There is, Sir. Dad, can we take him over to Mrs. Phillips?"

Dad agrees and drives us over to Rockwood Hill. Mrs.Phillips gives Robert Wakely the 8 x 10 of Bonnybelle, and I say, "She's the one who really saved John Henry's life. Will you make sure he knows that when he gets older?"

"You bet I will, Alec. Now there's just one more thing I need to see."

We take him out to the cemetery just north of town and show him Bonnybelle's grave. The stone, a simple flat gray marker, has just been put in place. It gives her name, the years of her birth and death, and one more word that I insist the carver add: *Heroine.*

"Bet that last word was your idea," Robert Wakely says.

"Yessir. That's what she was."

"She was indeed." He puts his hand on my right shoulder. It hurts a little, but I don't brush it off. "Son," he says. "I get the feelin' yer down on yerself 'cause yuh couldn't save her too."

"I tried, Mr. Wakely, but…"

"It's all right. John Henry's alive today 'cause yuh come back to take that second look an' roused his sister, an' then the two of yuh got him out. Yuh pulled off one miracle. Don't go a-hittin' yerself over the head 'cause yuh couldn't do two."

"But Bonnybelle's gone forever now, Mr. Wakely!" Lord! I'm close to crying again.

"Don't yuh be so sure of that! Her brother's alive, an' it looks like he's a-gonna have her looks an' her spunk." He chuckles. "We Wakely boys never had no trouble attractin' the purty gals. I reckon, come twenty years or so, there could be another li'l Bonnybelle Wakely come along—an' maybe a li'l Alec Lewis Wakely too."

Robert Wakely's words—so simple and yet so powerful—seem to dissolve the load of guilt that I've heaped on myself. *You're not dead after all, Bonnybelle! You'll live on in your brother and his children!* As he takes his hand away, my sense of failure falls off like ice suddenly melting. "Thank you, Mr. Wakely. Will you keep in touch?"

"Yer mama an' daddy's got our address. We'll write yuh ever' year. John Henry will too, soon as he's old enough." He ruffles my hair, just like Bonnybelle's dad did with hers. "Yer a fine young man, Alec. Woulda been proud to have yuh as kin."

****

The balance of 1953 passes quietly, for me at least. Only three more noteworthy things happen. The *Oregon Journal* pesents me with a lifesaving medal at a banquet in Portland. Janet attends with Mom and Dad and me. (I think she wants to make her eighth-grade boyfriend jealous.) At the ceremony they award two—a silver for me and a posthumous gold for Bonnybelle. We send it back to her uncle in Missouri, and at Christmas they send us a snapshot of John Henry holding it along with his sister's picture.

****

Christmas Eve: Usually I'm so keyed up that I don't get to sleep before midnight, but this year a strange tiredness comes over me early in the evening, and I hit the sack before nine that night. Mom is afraid I'm coming down with something, but I don't feel sick—just tired. I seem to fall asleep before I'm even aware of the familiar warmth and comfort of my bed.

Then, in the middle of the night, I wake up. Or at least, I *think* I wake up. I know I've been dreaming, but I can't quite remember what. You never can, once you're awake. I think I sit up. The night is absolutely still, but the echo of something remains—the last notes of a song. I focus as hard as I can and pull back three words, *"O night divine!"* The rest are gone, but that's *O Holy Night*, the carol Bonnybelle never got to sing. Is she singing or do I dream it all? Before I can decide, I'm asleep again. But I'm never bothered with dreams about her or the fire after that.

On Christmas morning I race downstairs to find a new Hoffman console televison set right where our old Philco used to dominate the room. The radio has been relegated to a distant corner, and already it looks shabby and forgotten.

"It'll be Monday before we can get it all hooked up," Dad says, "but I wanted you to see it. It's not quite the top of the line, but I think it will do."

We hurry over to Salem for a big Christmas brunch with Grandma and Grandpa Fullerton, followed by the presents. Then we return to Morrisonville for me to do the route. The papers have to go out, even on Christmas. It's a Friday, so I don't have to get started before three, and I only have thirty to deliver, since all the shops are closed.

I stop to wish the Lofgrens and Mrs. Phillips a Merry Christmas. Mr. Lofgren is back on his feet, but he still looks thin and pale. The shell of the old trailer is gone, with only a patch of bare ground to show where it once stood. I'm glad I don't have to see it anymore.

Mrs. Lofgren gives me some cookies and Mrs. Phillips adds a candy bar. I don't buy the big blue jawbreakers anymore. They just don't taste the same without Bonnybelle's germs and spit on them.

"You know something, Alec?" Mrs. Phillips says as she takes the paper. "I dreamed I heard Bonnybelle singing last night."

"That's funny. So did I. Was it *O Holy Night*?"

She gives me a strange look. "It was," she says. From somewhere back in the house, one of her grandbabies starts to squall. She wishes me Merry Christmas and leaves to deal with it. I shake my head and hurry to finish the route. Maybe it's just a coincidence.

And then again, maybe it isn't.

****

New Year's Eve: The year has come full circle, and I'm having a birthday once more. Aunt Emma Snyder sits at the piano again, but this year she is sober and doesn't offer to play *The Internationale*. "We have come through a bitter year," she says. "But a terrible war is over, and our boys are no longer being killed. We have a new President, England has crowned a new Queen, that terrible monster Stalin is dead and the world's highest mountain has finally been climbed. And, Alec, you have recorded it all.

I have. I have also fallen in love twice (or at least I think I have) and lost both girls—one forever and one probably so. But my private new year's resolution is to try again in 1954. Hey! Maybe third time will be lucky.

"I think a new year calls for a new song," Aunt Emma concludes. "Why don't you all join me in *God Bless America*? Then it will be time for Alec to get ready for bed and open his presents."

We belt it out twice and then I race upstairs. I know what's waiting for me when I come back down. Sure enough, Aunt Emma holds a box tied with a single ribbon and some small holes poked in it for ventilation. "Nature cooperated, Alec, but the *dog* (with a sarcastic glance at Dad) only had two puppies, and both were female. This one is definitely the better of the two.

I carefully open the box and inside is a beautiful springer spaniel pup. She looks to be about eight weeks old. "She hasn't been named yet," Aunt Emma says. "We thought you'd like to do that. Any ideas?"

The pup cocks its head to one side and gives me a cool, appraising stare—and I know exactly what to do. Robert Wakely's words are comforting, but I'm not going to wait twenty years. I lift the pup out of the box and kiss it right on the nose.

"Hello there, Bonnybelle!" I say, and the pup wiggles and licks my face.

The End